PONY
THE ANNUAL

First published in Great Britain in 2016
DJ Murphy (Publishers) Ltd

ISBN 978-0-9928279-3-9

Who did what in PONY – The Annual

Contributors Georgia Guerin, Laura Hodgson, Louise Kittle, Jessica Lewis, Victoria Rea, Lucy Turner, Tilly Berendt
Design Adam Witt
Published by DJ Murphy (Publishers) Ltd, Marlborough House, Headley Road, Grayshott, Surrey GU26 6LG

Printed by Graphicom via dell'Industria – 36100 Vicenza, Italy

Photography Bob Atkins, Steve Bardens, Trevor Meeks, shutterstock.com
Pages 6-7 Arnd Bronkhorst, James Jones Jr/shutterstock.com, Bob Langrish, Trevor Meeks
Pages 8-9 FEI/Arnd Bronkhorst/Pool Pic
Pages 18-19 Conny Sjostrom/shutterstock.com
Pages 20-21 Clive Chilvers/shutterstock.com, Debu55y/shutterstock.com, maziarz/shutterstock.com
Pages 30-31 Badminton Horse Trials, Mitsubishi Motors/Kit Houghton
Pages 48-49 Kevin Day/shutterstock.com, Flik47/shutterstock.com, James Jones Jr/shutterstock.com, Cedric Weber/shutterstock.com
Page 55 Steve Bardens
Pages 56-57 Zara Tindall is a Dodson & Horrell brand ambassador. With thanks to Dodson & Horrell for their help with this feature, dodsonandhorrell.com Photo: FEI/Arnd Bronkhorst/Pool Pic
Page 59 AK Photography
Pages 70-71 i4lcocl2/shutterstock.com, Png Studio Photography/ shutterstock.com, Wolfilser/shutterstock.com
Pages 82-83 FEI/Amy Dragoo-arnd.nl
Pages 94-95 Bob Langrish

Front cover image Bob Atkins
Illustrators (pages 102-103) Helena Öhmark and Rebecca Öhmark

PONY magazine is published every four weeks.
To find out more about PONY magazine, visit ponymag.com

PONY

THE ANNUAL

2017

Publishers of PONY magazine

PONY THE ANNUAL 2017

INSIDE YOUR ANNUAL...

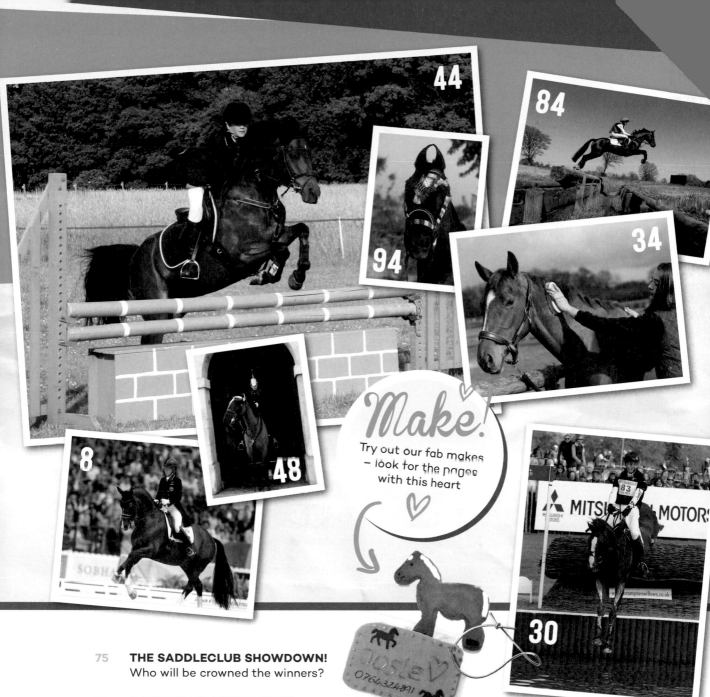

Make!
Try out our fab makes – look for the pages with this heart ♡

Valegro

Everything you've ever wanted to know about the dressage superstar!

Stable name: Blueberry • **Discipline:** Dressage
Ridden by: Charlotte Dujardin

Valegro was born on 5 July 2002, in the Netherlands. He was sired by the famous dressage stallion Negro, but he wasn't always a brilliant dressage horse! He failed his stallion grading as a two-year-old and his owner, Olympic rider Carl Hester, thought that he would be too small to be successful.

Now 16.2hh, the gorgeous bay gelding has definitely proven everyone wrong!

Perfect partners

Carl originally planned to sell Blueberry, but decided to keep him when his first young horse classes went well.

He then gave the ride to Charlotte Dujardin, his talented pupil, who had been successful in the show ring as a child. Together she and Blueberry climbed through the levels and the rest, of course, is history!

Cheeky chap!

Blueberry has a big personality and loves food more than anything else. His favourite treats are carrots, Polos and extra-strong mints - but he's not fussed with soft mints! He loves to dunk his haylage into his water bucket and has been known to sneak a mouthful of the decorative flowers at dressage shows!

Bold as brass

He may have won every major competition in the world, but Blueberry is definitely not a diva! He loves to go hacking twice a week and is notorious for eating leaves out of the hedgerows as he goes. He's so brave that he's often used to give young horses a lead past spooky things – but his walk is so big that they sometimes struggle to keep up!

Blueberry likes to stick to a routine and is ridden first thing in the morning so he can spend the day relaxing in the field and having an afternoon nap.

Winning in Las Vegas!

RECORD BREAKERS

87.46%
Grand Prix

88.022%
Grand Prix Special

94.30%
Grand Prix Freestyle

A slightly longer and more advanced version of the Grand Prix

Blueberry and Charlotte have broken loads of records with their incredible dressage scores!

Dressage to music

LIKES

- food, especially mints!
- massage sessions with his physiotherapist, Marnie
- hacking – he's very nosy and likes to have a look up other people's driveways!
- hanging out in the field in his zebra print fly rug!
- rolling in the mud right after a bath
- a good fuss and a sugar cube from his super-groom, Alan

DISLIKES

- being clipped – he's really ticklish!
- being tacked up – he'd rather just get on with work

KEEPING UP WITH VALEGRO

When he's not competing, Blueberry has a busy schedule to stick to – he's schooled four days a week, goes hacking two days a week, regularly works out on Hartpury College's water treadmill, and sees a physiotherapist for massage sessions. Phew!

TOP RESULTS

2016 Rio Olympics – team silver and individual gold
2015 Aachen European Championships – team silver and individual gold
2014 Normandy World Equestrian Games – team and individual gold
2013 Herning European Championships – team bronze and individual gold
2012 London Olympics – team and individual gold
2011 Rotterdam European Championships - team gold

☆

Staying straight

This is a great exercise to test how straight you and your pony are – and to improve it if needed!

Set up three pairs of parallel poles three paces apart along the centre line. In walk, ride up the centre line at A, between the poles. Change the rein when you get to C, and repeat on the other rein.

Your aim is to stay perfectly straight between the poles and not drift to one side or wobble between them. You also need to make sure your pony is straight through his whole body and not just his neck.

If you don't quite manage this, it shows that you're not sitting straight in the saddle. Remember to keep an even weight in both stirrups and wrap your legs around your pony's sides. Keep a soft, even contact to allow him to walk on through the poles.

When you've mastered this exercise in walk, try it in trot, then canter. You'll be able to ride a perfect straight line before you know it.

TOP TIP
Make sure you warm up your pony properly before starting polework exercises.

PERFECT

Create an adjustable stride

This exercise will help you create a canter stride that you can lengthen and shorten, and will show if your pony is listening to you.

Place two poles down the long side of your arena, 13.5m apart. This should be roughly five comfortable canter strides, but you may need to roll the poles closer together or further away based on your pony's stride length.

Practise cantering over the poles, aiming to fit in five canter strides. Once you and your pony are confident, practise shortening his stride to fit in six strides, then lengthening to fit in four strides. Remember that lengthening and shortening should not result in a change of speed!

It's likely you'll need to practise this exercise several times to perfect it and to feel comfortable adding in or taking out a stride. The key thing to remember is to make sure your pony is balanced at all times and not rushing through the poles.

Improve your suppleness

This exercise will improve your pony's suppleness and engagement, as well as making sure you're balanced in the saddle.

Set up four poles in a cross formation on a 20-metre circle. Ride a circle in walk, over the middle of each pole. Your pony should be straight as he steps over the pole, before bending towards the next. Ride the circle two or three times, then repeat on the other rein.

Look towards the next pole as you ride this exercise, to help your pony bend. You should aim to be riding the same number of strides between each pole, to ensure your pony is balanced and in an even rhythm.

Once you're confident, this exercise can be done in trot and canter. Only ride it a couple of times on each rein before moving on, as it's hard work for your pony.

TOP TIP
Keep it varied — don't go over the same exercise again and again, as your pony will become bored and switch off.

POLEWORK

Winter riding doesn't have to be boring! Spice up your schooling with our fab polework exercises to keep you and your pony interested

Helpful half-halts

If you find your pony rushing through these exercises, use half-halts to keep him balanced and listening to your aids.

To ride a half-halt, wrap your legs around your pony's sides and close your hands around the reins to contain his energy, then release.

TOP TIP
To shorten your pony's stride, keep your leg on to maintain impulsion, but use half-halts to contain his energy. To lengthen his stride, keep a soft contact and wrap your legs around him to ask him to open up and extend his stride. Don't push him on too much, though, otherwise he'll rush and become unbalanced.

A DAY IN THE LIFE OF A PONY!

We all love having a chat with our fave pony and there are times when he really seems to understand what we're saying. But do you know what he's thinking? We followed gorgeous Digby for a day with his owner, Hannah, to find out

Hello, I'm Digby!

PONY EVOLUTION

Way back before ponies became domesticated, we grazed in herds, walking for miles every day. It's important to think about how us ponies used to behave in the wild when it comes to working out what we're thinking.

As herd and prey animals, we feel safest in groups. This means that when you take your fave pony out of his herd, he's likely to feel more vulnerable and nervous.

Everyone wants their fave pony to be as happy and relaxed as possible when they're riding and handling him, so follow my advice, straight from the horse's mouth, to find out what us ponies think about from day-to-day!

DID YOU KNOW?
All ponies are individuals with different personalities, just like people!

Stabling

I'm normally stabled at night with the other ponies at the yard. I love coming in for a snooze and a lie-down, but I do get worried if I can't see any of my field mates, so make sure your fave pony can keep an eye on his friends when he's stabled to keep him relaxed!

My fab owner, Hannah, always makes sure I have a full haynet when I come in, which lasts me through the night. I'd have a very rumbly tummy otherwise, as it's natural for us ponies to graze regularly. My next-door neighbour (and BFF!), Bertie, has his hay double-netted to slow him down when he's eating it, otherwise he guzzles it all in a couple of hours – this is a good way to make sure your pony's hay lasts longer.

TOP TIP
If your pony is grumpy and bargy in his stable, try to keep him turned out for as long as possible to keep his stress levels to a minimum.

Yummmm!

Grooming

I luuurrve being groomed! It's a great way for me to bond with Hannah, plus, she gives all my itchy spots a good scratch. I always let her know just how much I appreciate it by grooming her back, just like I do with Bertie in the field!

DID YOU KNOW?
Mutual grooming, when ponies groom each other, releases chemicals called endorphins, which makes us feel happy and relaxed.

Tacking up

Hannah's always really careful when she tacks me up – there's nothing worse than someone throwing my saddle on and yanking the girth up or hitting my teeth with the bit. She always makes sure everything is fitted correctly and my girth isn't pinching before she gets on, and takes the time to check my reactions.

If I have a sore back or teeth, I show it by swishing my tail and looking grumpy, or if something is really hurting I might try to kick out or bite. It's a right pain not being able to talk to you humans, you know, so I've found this is the best way to communicate!

Riding

As well as being handsome, I'm also super-talented and pick up on things really quickly when I'm being ridden. Hannah always makes sure our schooling sessions finish on a good note – I like to have a good think about what I've learnt when I'm dozing in my stable, so if something hasn't gone well, I don't look forward to being ridden the next time. I love being told I've done something well (who doesn't?), so when Hannah gives me a gentle pat and praises me, I can't wait to give it a go again!

Like most ponies, I get bored easily, though, so I really enjoy doing lots of different things. It's dull doing the same thing over and over again, but I'm lucky that Hannah keeps it interesting. We perfected our dressage yesterday and today we're going hacking – my fave thing! There's nothing better than having a good nose around the area and going for a fun canter.

DID YOU KNOW?

Ponies have evolved to learn things quickly, because if they made the same mistake twice in the wild, it could be a matter of life or death.

What's that?

DID YOU KNOW?

Your pony can tell a lot from your tone of voice. If he's scared of something, talk to him in a low, soothing voice to calm him down – it'll help keep you relaxed as well!

Spooking

Okay, okay, so I know I come across as confident and brave, but even I get scared sometimes. I'm used to things looking the same, but when there's something new in my field or out hacking, it's only natural for me to be suspicious of it!

Remember not to get cross if your fave pony spooks at something – it only makes us more worried if we're told off for having a look. Plus, us ponies have a much better sense of hearing and smell than you humans, so sometimes we notice things you don't! Once I've worked out it's not scary, I'm happy to walk past and Hannah always gives me a pat to reassure me.

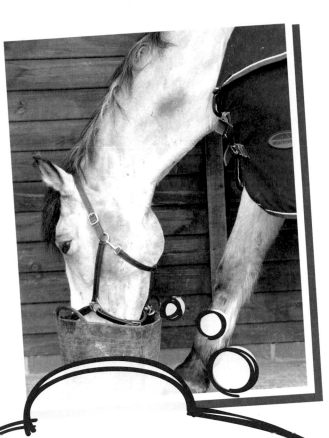

Rolling

If I had to rank my top five fave things, rolling would definitely be up near the top. I always look for the muddiest patch in the field to have a roll in – not only is it fab for having a good scratch, but being covered in mud means Hannah has to spend more time grooming me! I also find having lots of caked-on mud means those pesky flies can't get to me as easily in the summer.

DID YOU KNOW?

Ponies sometimes have certain places in the field where they enjoy rolling. Ponies who are turned out together often queue up to roll in the same place one after another.

It's thought to be a sign of good health if a pony can roll over from one side to the other, without having to get up in-between.

Feeding

I think about food a *lot*. I can't help it, as I was designed to spend most of the day grazing and having a good munch on grass (and sometimes the odd branch out hacking – whoops!).

To stay healthy, us ponies need plenty of forage such as grass, hay or haylage. We also prefer to have any hard food that we need split up into small meals across the day – I have mine at breakfast and dinner.

Sleeping

Us ponies like to doze every so often throughout the day and night, rather than one big sleep at night like you humans. We take short naps while standing up, so we can move off quickly in case we're spooked by something.

For us to have a deep sleep, we need to lie down, but we don't do this unless we feel safe. My safe place is in my stable and I can have a proper sleep in there. Sometimes I sleep out in the field if it's a dry day and Bertie's there to stand over me, but I hate lying down in the field if I'm on my own or it's wet – no one wants a soggy tummy, yuck!

Turnout

In my opinion, there's nothing better than being turned out in the field with my best mate, Bertie. We love to mess around having a play in the field – it's our time to have fun.

Make sure that your fave pony gets on with his field mates, though. It's no fun for us if we're not friends with our companions, as we might fight with each other, which means we can't really relax as we're always keeping an eye open in case of trouble.

Bertie and I don't have that problem, though. We're always looking out for each other when we're turned out – we're like two peas in a pod!

Make!
PONY COOKIES

Surprise your friends at the yard with cookies that look exactly like their ponies!

You will need...
- ☑ mixing bowl
- ☑ wooden spoon
- ☑ sieve
- ☑ rolling pin
- ☑ pony-shaped cutter
- ☑ non-stick baking tray
- ☑ cooling rack
- ☑ photos of your friends' ponies
- ☑ icing in colours that match your friends' ponies – white, milk and dark chocolate, and caramel-flavoured writing icing is ideal
- ☑ cookie ingredients –
  250g butter, softened
  140g caster sugar
  1 egg yolk
  2tsp vanilla extract
  300g plain flour

How to do it!

Step 1

Thoroughly mix the butter and sugar in a bowl, then add the egg yolk and vanilla extract, and mix it all together. Sift over the flour in stages and stir it in to form a firm dough.

Step 2

Sprinkle some flour on the work surface and rolling pin. Place the dough on the work surface and roll it out until it's 1–2mm thick. Use the cutter to cut out pony shapes, then place them on the baking tray.

Step 3

Ask an adult to help you bake them at 160°C for 12–15 minutes or until golden. Once cooked, take them off the baking tray and place them on a rack to cool.

Step 4

Once cool, use the photos of your friends' ponies to ice each cookie to look just like them!

BREEDS

>> ICELANDICS

Known as the horse of the Vikings, the Icelandic is the only breed of horse from Iceland

> HISTORY

The Icelandic is an ancient breed. Its ancestors were horses that the Norse people took to Iceland more than 1,000 years ago. Horses were the only way of getting around Iceland's rocky, icy landscape, and were also used to herd sheep and plough the fields. Today, most Icelandics don't have to work like their ancestors, and are mainly used for competition and leisure riding.

> STANDARDS

Icelandics are usually between 12 and 14.2hh. In other breeds, this would class as a pony, but Icelandics are always referred to as horses because there is no word in Icelandic for pony.

They have beautiful, straight faces with wide foreheads, short and muscular necks, low withers and deep chests. Their backs are long, broad and muscular, which makes them great weight carriers. Icelandics have thick, bushy manes and low-set tails to help keep out the worst of the winter snow and wind.

The breed is represented by The International Federation of Icelandic Horse Associations.

A PURE BREED

When the plague broke out in Europe in the 14th Century, Iceland put itself into quarantine to avoid the infection. For many years, no one could come or go, and even today there are restrictions on importing and exporting live animals and plants. As a result, Icelandic horses have never been cross-bred with other horses, so they have remained pure for more than a thousand years.

SURVIVAL OF THE FITTEST

Iceland isn't the easiest place for a horse to survive. The island is volcanic and there aren't any trees to shelter under. Despite the tough conditions, Icelandic horses are extremely hardy and tend to live well into their 30s. Only the strongest horses could withstand the harsh Icelandic climate, where temperatures can reach lows of -30°C!

Brrr, it's a bit chilly!

Skeið is super-fast!

TROT ON!

Icelandics have two extra gaits in addition to walk, trot and canter. The first is a four-beat gait known as tölt, which all Icelandics are born with. The footfall pattern is the same as walk, but it's a lot faster.

The second is called skeið, flugskeið or flying pace. It's a two-beat gait with a moment of suspension between footfalls (left hind and left front, suspension, right hind and right front). It's very fast, with some horses able to reach up to 30mph! Skeið isn't a natural gait and not all Icelandic horses can do it.

Today, Icelandics are mainly used for competition and pleasure riding. Racing is popular and so are performance classes that show off the gaits. Most pacing horses are raced in harness, but Icelandics are raced under saddle.

CLEVER COATS!

Like other breeds that live in cold, harsh climates, Icelandics have a double-layered coat. The under layer is really soft and fluffy for warmth, and the outer layer is thick, long and waterproof – and can be literally any colour. If you visit Iceland and see a herd of horses, there will be every colour imaginable!

Because they grow such a thick coat, Icelandics will need clipping during winter if they are being worked a lot. Like any breed, they should never be turned out wet and sweaty or they will catch a chill.

TEMPERAMENT

They are a brave and bold little horse, but also friendly and reliable. They are very sturdy and sure-footed, both in temperament and in their way of going.

NOM NOM!

Icelandics can survive on very little food. The worst thing you can do is overfeed them. As long as you have enough grazing, an Icelandic should require very little extra feeding.

HORSE JOBS

MARVELLOUS MOUNTED POLICE

Police horses are big, bold and brave – and super-handsome, too!

DID YOU KNOW?

The Mounted Branch of the Metropolitan Police was set up more than 250 years ago to help deal with highwaymen who travelled on horses, robbing people passing through London.

Many police horses retire to horse charities where they can live out their years in comfort with all their friends!

In some Middle Eastern countries, as well as horses, mounted police ride camels, as they're better suited to the environmental conditions.

One of the biggest police horses in the UK was Big Klyde, who was a whopping 19hh! He retired in 2012 after more than 10 years of service.

Want to sign up?

To join the mounted police, you'll need to qualify as a normal police officer first. After three years, you're able to specialise in an area, such as the mounted police. Believe it or not, no previous riding experience is necessary!

It's not all work!

The Metropolitan Police Activity ride has become a famous attraction at shows such as Olympia and the Horse of the Year Show. This nail-biting display shows off the accuracy and trust between police horse and police officer, and is seriously impressive! Not only do the riders wow the crowds by taking their saddles off while riding, the horses even jump through rings of fire!

DID YOU KNOW? Mounted police officers clean their tack every day to keep it in tip-top condition!

THE DAILY DUTIES

Mounted police have an important role in a number of duties. They're chosen when their height and ability to direct crowds gives them an advantage over officers on the ground and police cars. Duties include...

● **sporting events** – police horses are often seen at football matches and other large sporting events. Their height allows officers to keep an eye on everyone in the crowd and they can be seen more easily – handy for giving directions and orders.

● **crowd control** – the large size of police horses can intimidate troublemakers and the horses are able to break up crowds more effectively than non-mounted officers. Horses wear special riot kit, which includes a face mask and padded boots, to keep them protected.

● **patrolling** – an average patrol is around 3–4 hours and allows mounted officers to help stop crimes taking place. On average, they cover around 10 miles on each patrol.

Training

Training is tailored to each horse, with three phases...

● the first is the **red phase,** where the basics are established – this includes standing still and general stable manners

● the **amber phase** comes next, where the horses are introduced to different environments, including open spaces and water, as well as getting used to wearing uniform

● the **green phase** is the final stage of training, where the horses become used to going on patrols, heavy traffic and being ridden in the dark. They're also introduced to sound recordings of military bands, crowds and trains

Once these three phases have been passed, the horse is issued to an officer, where he's gradually introduced to real-life situations, including patrols, smaller football matches and escorting the military. When he's confident with this, he'll begin to be used for larger-scale events and crowd control, and be a fully-fledged police horse!

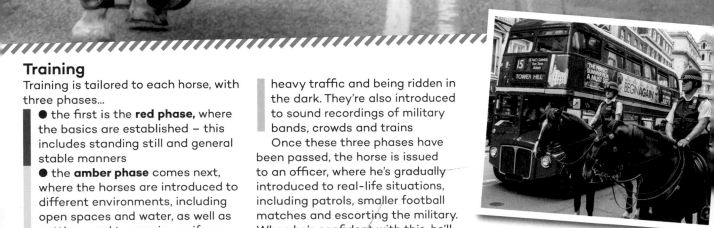

Police horses have to remain calm in heavy traffic

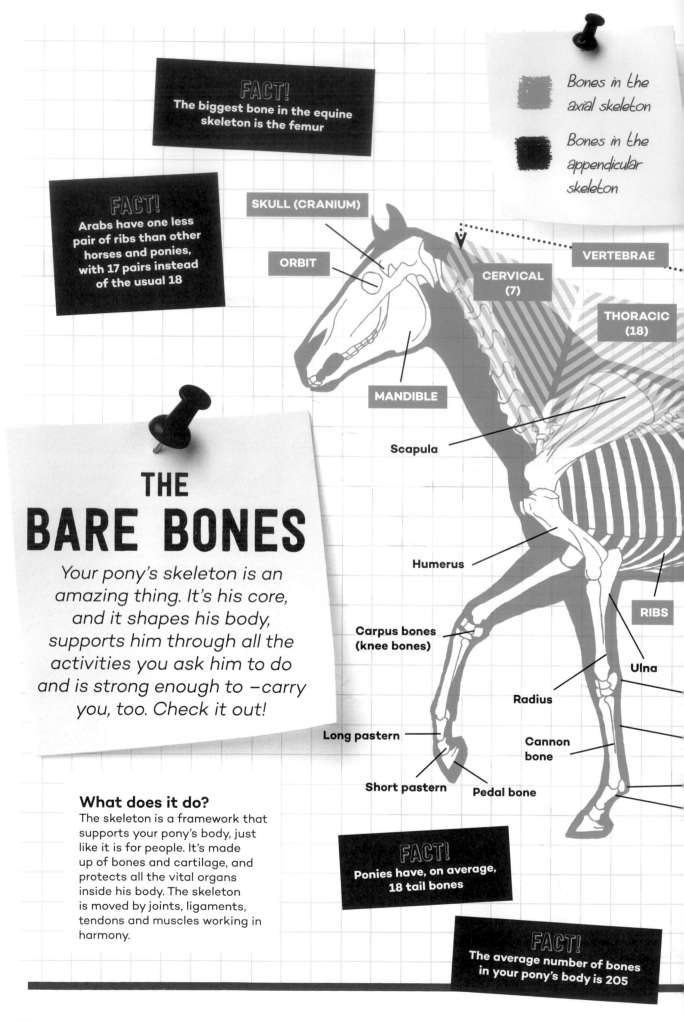

FACT!
The biggest bone in the equine skeleton is the femur

Bones in the axial skeleton

Bones in the appendicular skeleton

FACT!
Arabs have one less pair of ribs than other horses and ponies, with 17 pairs instead of the usual 18

SKULL (CRANIUM)

ORBIT

CERVICAL (7)

VERTEBRAE

THORACIC (18)

MANDIBLE

Scapula

THE
BARE BONES

Your pony's skeleton is an amazing thing. It's his core, and it shapes his body, supports him through all the activities you ask him to do and is strong enough to –carry you, too. Check it out!

Humerus

Carpus bones (knee bones)

RIBS

Ulna

Radius

Long pastern

Cannon bone

Short pastern

Pedal bone

What does it do?
The skeleton is a framework that supports your pony's body, just like it is for people. It's made up of bones and cartilage, and protects all the vital organs inside his body. The skeleton is moved by joints, ligaments, tendons and muscles working in harmony.

FACT!
Ponies have, on average, 18 tail bones

FACT!
The average number of bones in your pony's body is 205

The sciency bit!

There are two parts to your pony's skeleton – the axial skeleton and the appendicular skeleton.

Axial skeleton
It's made up of...
● the skull, which protects his brain
● the vertebrae, which runs from his skull to his tail and protects his spinal cord
● the ribcage, which protects his heart, lungs and digestive system

Appendicular skeleton
It's made up of...
● the shoulders and forelegs
● the pelvis and hindlegs

Bone basics
Bones are made up of collagen, calcium and phosphorus. Collagen is a tissue made of protein, and calcium and phosphorous are minerals. Bones provide support and protection, and together make up the whole skeleton.

How they work
Bones are covered with a very tough, thin membrane called the periosteum. Tendons and ligaments attach to the periosteum, which allows the bones to move. Bones contain marrow, which produces the red blood cells that are essential for carrying oxygen around your pony's body.

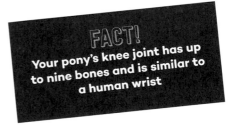

DID YOU KNOW?
Bones act as a store for minerals

Joints explained
A joint is where two or more bones meet. They enable the skeleton to move. Cartilage is a smooth, tough substance that covers the ends of bones to stop them rubbing together. In some joints, such as the hocks, knees and fetlocks, a joint oil called synovial fluid covers them to help them move easily.

FACT!
Your pony's knee joint has up to nine bones and is similar to a human wrist

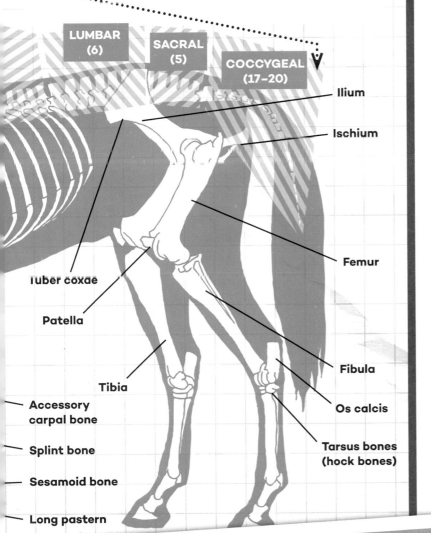

LUMBAR (6)
SACRAL (5)
COCCYGEAL (17–20)

Ilium
Ischium
Femur
Tuber coxae
Patella
Fibula
Tibia
Os calcis
Accessory carpal bone
Splint bone
Tarsus bones (hock bones)
Sesamoid bone
Long pastern

MY CHARITY CHAMPION

When Izzy decided to give a rescue pony a forever home, she never dreamt she'd have a champion on her hands!

After my gorgeous first pony, Badger, was put to sleep due to old age, I felt like there was a big, pony-shaped hole in my life. I'd had a pony ever since I could remember and things just weren't the same without one. Luckily, my parents agreed I could get another pony.

I started searching through magazines and websites that advertised ponies for sale, and decided to put up a wanted advert in the local tack shop. I carefully crafted my advert, describing the pony I longed for.

While I was pinning up my advert, a leaflet with a sad-looking pony on the front caught my eye. It was for an equine charity who rescued neglected or abused ponies, nursed them back to health, then found them forever homes. Staring into the sad eyes of the cover pony, I knew what I had to do. I took down my advert and rushed home to call the charity.

Charity visit
Mum spoke to the charity's rehoming centre. She described our yard and the type of pony I was looking for – a sweet-natured native, approximately 14.2hh – and added the fact I was partial to bays! I waited, anxiously, for Mum to finish the call and tell me everything the charity had said. "They need to come and visit our yard," Mum explained, "so they can decide whether it's suitable for one of their ponies." My heart sank. What if they didn't like us? "They're coming on Tuesday," Mum said.

Tuesday seemed to take forever to arrive, but when it finally did, I felt a wave of butterflies as a big white truck with the charity's logo on the side pulled into the yard. The driver's door swung open and a lady jumped out, holding a clipboard. "Hi!" she beamed, enthusiastically. "I'm Donna, the centre's manager. Nice to meet you." She shook both our hands and grinned.

We spent over an hour showing Donna the fields, school, nearest bridlepath, hay supply and feed room.

"Well, thanks for the tour," Donna said, as we arrived back at her truck. "We'll be in contact and, if we decide you're suitable rehomers, we'll arrange for you to visit the centre." The butterflies fluttered again – if we're accepted, I could meet my new pony soon!

My dream pony
The day after, Mum received an email inviting us to visit the charity. My heart leapt – they liked us!

As soon as we arrived, I smiled as ponies popped their heads over their stable doors. Each stable had a board hanging up outside with the pony's name, feeding details and any special notes about them. As we walked through the yard, Donna explained the stories of each of the rescue ponies. I felt a lump rising in my throat – how could such lovely ponies be neglected? My thoughts were interrupted by Donna, who suddenly sounded quite excited. "Now, after we visited and you described the sort of pony you were looking for, this is the one I had in mind. Meet Finn."

I approached the stable slowly and, as I got close, a pony with a shiny bay head and gleaming eyes appeared. He was munching on a mouthful of hay, and had bits of it scattered over his face and in his forelock. I giggled immediately.

"He's quite a character!" Donna laughed. "He belonged to an elderly lady whose grandchildren used to ride him, but they lost interest and she struggled to look after him, so he got quite thin and had bad feet. She agreed to sign him over to our care so we could find him a new owner who can take care of him."

"He's beautiful," I whispered.

bay pony · shiny coat · 14.2hh · nice paces · friendly · fun-loving

❝ *I felt a lump rising in my throat — how could such lovely ponies be neglected?* **❞**

"So do you want to ride him?" Donna nodded towards me. She didn't need to ask twice.

I rode Finn in the outdoor arena in walk, trot and canter and, although he felt a bit unbalanced at times, he was so comfy and really willing. "He's definitely been schooled," Donna explained, "I think he's even been to a few shows in his time."

I spent an hour or so grooming Finn after my ride. He was so sweet, nuzzling me each time I went near his head. I couldn't help falling in love with him.

Mum and I arranged to see Finn again the following weekend, then we could decide whether we wanted to take him on. I reluctantly hugged Finn goodbye, and began counting the days until I'd see him again.

After visiting Finn for a second time, we agreed to rehome him. I was so excited to have my own pony again, but I felt nervous as Mum had explained it was a big responsibility to take on a rescue pony. I'd need to be prepared to go the extra mile to take care of Finn and give him the attention he deserved.

Finn's secret

The day the charity was due to deliver Finn, loads of questions ran through my head. What if he didn't like it here? What if we didn't get on? Butterflies swirled in my tummy, but by the time the lorry arrived and I saw Finn's gorgeous face again, they disappeared.

He settled in really well and I know we'd made the best decision. He loved his new stable and even let the yard cat, Rocky, share it sometimes! It took a few months to build up his fitness, but once I had, he was just like any other pony.

I rode Finn in the school one day and another girl at the yard had left a few fences up. "Why don't you try popping Finn over a fence or two?" Mum suggested.

I hadn't jumped in a while and felt a pang of nerves as I turned Finn towards a cross-pole. He cantered confidently towards it and cleared it effortlessly. I turned to a small upright, Finn pricked his ears and again cleared the fence with ease.

"Wow!" Mum said, "he can jump!"

"Good boy, Finn!" I smiled and gave him a huge pat.

Finn's ears were pricked as he trotted back to the gate. "I think he likes it!" I laughed.

I had a few lessons on Finn and found that we both loved jumping! We were becoming a confident partnership and, after one particularly successful lesson, my instructor, Liz, suggested entering a showjumping class at a local show. Liz assured me that after Finn's rehabilitation at the centre and all the work I'd done getting his fitness up, he could do anything any other pony could. So I agreed to enter.

It was clear Finn knew how to jump

Our best day

The day of the show quickly arrived and I suddenly felt nervous again. What if it was too much for Finn and I? What if the other girls on their fancy ponies laughed at us? All the negative thoughts whizzed around in my head but I managed to shake them. I had to believe in myself and Finn.

My hands were wobbly as our number was called, and Finn and I trotted into the jumping arena. We picked up canter as the bell rang and I steered towards the first fence. Three, two, one... I counted the strides in my head. Finn met the fence on a perfect stride and sailed over it. He did the same at the next fence and the next. My confidence soared with each successful jump and I was disappointed it was over when we crossed the finish. I couldn't believe it – a clear round! Finn and I were unstoppable!

I was called into the jump-off and my heart pounded as I navigated Finn around the course. He skipped round the twisty course and jumped his heart out for another clear. I patted him until I couldn't feel my hand anymore and almost fell off when we were announced as the winners! I threw my arms round Finn's neck as I clutched the red rosette I'd been given and even shed a couple of tears on our lap of honour. I was so proud of my champion rescue pony!

I've entered a few more competitions with Finn and, even though nothing can compare to how I felt the day we won our first rosette, we've never looked back. I know rehoming Finn was the best decision I ever made. I gave him the forever home he deserves. I would say to anyone to always consider a rescue pony and, besides, you might find you've got a superstar on your hands – just like I did!

Finn and I flew round the course!

BADMINTON HORSE TRIALS: through the years

1949

The first year the event ran. It only had 22 competitors and just 14 of them managed to finish the cross-country course! This gave the event its reputation as one of the greatest tests of horse and rider ability.

1981

Lucinda Green wins the event for the sixth time, giving her the record of the most Badminton wins ever!

1988

Ian Stark becomes the only rider to come first and second, winning on Sir Wattie and coming second on Glenburnie.

DID YOU KNOW?

Prize money for the winner in 1949 was a measly £150 – that wouldn't even cover the entry fee today! These days, the winning prize money is £80,000.

1955

Badminton Horse Trials goes on tour! It was held at Windsor Castle by invitation of Her Majesty the Queen.

1959

Sheila Willcox becomes the first (and only, so far) rider to win the event an impressive three times in a row!

1956

Badminton Horse Trials is first shown on television, broadcast by the BBC.

1994

The year the oldest horse won the event, 16-year-old Horton Point, ridden by Mark Todd.

1995

Mark Todd famously rides around most of the cross-country course with only one stirrup – impressive!

Badminton is the event every top rider wants to win! We take a look at the thrills and spills through the event's history

2003

Pippa Funnell wins on Supreme Rock for the second year in a row, setting her up for her Rolex Grand Slam of eventing win later in the year at Burghley.

2006

The event runs in short format for the first time. In previous years, riders completed roads and tracks and steeplechase before the cross-country phase (known as long format), where they would ride a combined distance of up to 13.2km (just over eight miles). Roads and tracks and steeplechase are no longer part of the event.

2015

Chilli Morning, ridden by William Fox-Pitt, becomes the first stallion to win the event.

2014

Giuseppe della Chiesa becomes the new cross-country course designer and builds a mega-difficult course. Only 37 riders complete the cross-country, with 43 retiring or eliminated on course.

2016

Michael Jung makes history as the first German to win the event, as well as breaking the record for the best-ever score at Badminton. He also becomes the second person to win the Rolex Grand Slam of Eventing, which hasn't been done in more than 10 years!

2008

Nicolas Touzaint is the first Frenchman to win Badminton.

1 Pack a picnic
Grab a selection of your fave snacks, a tasty drink and some of your pony's fave treats, pack them into a saddlebag or bum bag and away you go! Put a headcollar on over your pony's bridle and clip a wrapped-up leadrope to your saddle, so you can dismount and have your snacks halfway round your ride.

DONE

2 Take a leap
If you love jumping, there's nothing more fun than popping over a few logs while you're out hacking. Make sure the ground on the take-off and landing is safe before you jump, though.

DONE

3 Power hack
Going on a fast hack with a friend is great fun for you and your ponies. Choose your route carefully to include wide paths with good ground so your long canters aren't interrupted. Make sure your pony is fit enough for the route you've planned.

DONE

4 Group ride
Get your bezzies and their fave ponies together, and organise a group ride. Most ponies love hacking in company and it'll be fun for you to go hacking with your friends, too.

DONE

WATCHPOINT!
Some ponies might get very excited about going hacking in a big group, especially if your ride is fast, so be ready for him to be livelier than usual!

5 Go galloping!
There's no denying that galloping is great fun! If you're lucky enough to have some open fields or purpose-built gallops near you, then go for a blast! If not, some gallops are available to hire out, so why not find out which are nearest to you and take a trip? It'll be well worth it!

DONE

6 Chase the sun
There's nothing like riding through beautiful countryside in glorious sunshine, but the sunshine part isn't something that Britain always has to offer. Hacking in another country is an amazing experience and you'll get to ride different types of ponies, too. Get Googling to find the perfect destination for you!

DONE

7 Take a dip
If you've got a stream or ford near your yard, why not take your pony for a dip? For those who like getting their toes wet it'll be a refreshing treat. For ponies who aren't so keen on water, it's good practice for them without being under any pressure. Make sure you check the footing first to make sure the ground at the edge of the water is safe.

DONE

8 Map it
Fancy yourself as a pro navigator? Get your hands on a map of your local area and plan a new hacking route. You might discover bridlepaths you didn't know existed!

DONE

9 Back to school

It's easy to ride more lazily than normal out hacking, but schooling on a hack can be loads of fun and is super-handy if you don't have access to an arena. Ask your pony to be purposeful in each pace, no dawdling! Be strict about when and where you make your transitions – use trees or logs as markers. And why not try a few lateral movements to keep your pony interested? Ask him to move from one side of a path to the other and back again.

DONE ☐

12 Try TREC

TREC is an organisation that runs competitions where riders and their ponies compete in orienteering and obstacle phases. You'll get to go hacking in new places and might even win a rosette! You can compete as an individual or in pairs, so why not ask a friend to enter, too?

DONE ☐

13 Super seasons

Enjoy hacking in every season. Spring is fab as the weather gets warmer and wildlife emerges. Summer is full of long, warm evenings and green surroundings. Trotting through paths of fallen leaves in autumn is really cool and, although the cold might not be everyone's idea of fun, a hack on a crisp, winters' day can be pretty awesome!

DONE ☐

15 FAB hacking MUST-DOS!

How many of these awesome hacking activities have you tried? Have loads of fun checking them off until you've done them all!

10 Box up

If you've got limited hacking around your yard, find out where the best local hacking routes are, box up your fave pony and go exploring! If you haven't got your own transport, ask some of your friends from the yard if they fancy the idea and club together to hire transport.

DONE ☐

TOP TIP!
Make sure you check there's a safe place to park the trailer or horsebox while you're out riding.

14 Brave the beach

Cantering across a sandy beach and splashing through shallow waves is a dream for most riders. So why not make it a reality? Remember to check the tide times and, depending on the rules of your nearest beach, the times you're allowed to ride on it.

DONE ☐

11 On your own

Heading out on the bridlepaths with your pony can be super-peaceful and a great way for you to spend time together. You'll learn lots about each other, too.

DONE ☐

15 Follow the leader

If you don't have your own pony to ride out on or if you fancy a change of scenery, why not contact your local riding centre and book a ride? A qualified instructor will lead the ride so you won't have to worry about navigating and you'll get to experience riding a new pony in a new place – totally cool!

DONE ☐

Spring GROOMING

Forget spring cleaning, how about spring grooming? Spring is the perfect season to get stuck into some serious grooming with your fave pony!

Step 1
Make sure your pony is tied up securely before you begin grooming.

Step 2
Pick out his feet with a hoof pick. Remember to use a downwards motion and be careful of your pony's sensitive frog.

Step 3
Use a dandy brush to remove dirt and mud. Take care not to use it on his face and ears, and be gentle on sensitive areas such as his belly and legs.

Step 4
Use a rubber curry comb to loosen hair in places where your pony isn't clipped. Move the comb over your pony's coat in a circular motion and brush off loose hair that gathers with a flick brush.

Step 5
Use a flick brush to get rid of any stubborn loose hairs and dust that remain.

Step 6
Give your pony an all-over groom with the body brush. It'll remove scurf and dirt from his coat. Be quite firm with the brush – it'll get your pony clean and give him a mini-massage, too.

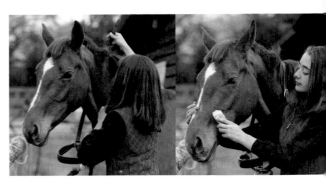

Step 7
To groom your pony's face, untie his leadrope so it's through the tie ring but not knotted and fasten his headcollar around his neck. Use gentle strokes with a face brush to groom his face, poll and ears. Take extra care around his sensitive eyes.

Step 8
Comb your pony's mane and forelock with a mane comb to remove knots.

Step 9
Groom your pony's tail with a specially-designed tail brush so you don't pull out his tail hairs. Remember to stand to one side of him as you do it.

Step 10
Sponge your pony's eyes and nose using a damp sponge. Take extra care around his eyes as they're very sensitive. Using a different sponge, clean your pony's dock. Make sure you clean the area under his tail, too.

Step 11
To achieve a high-shine finish, apply a coat spray. Avoid applying it to his saddle patch, though, as it will make the area slippery.

Voilà! A perfectly groomed, shiny pony!

Step 12
Apply a hoof moisturiser to your pony's feet to make him look really smart!

GROOMING GONE WRONG!

What not to do...

Don't keep your pony at arm's length when sponging his eyes and nose. You don't have any control over him and if he moves his head quickly he could knock you. You're much safer standing close to the side of him with your hand around his nose for control.

Brushing your pony's tail with a plastic curry comb could break the hairs and spoil the look of his tail.

Never groom your pony's face with a plastic curry comb – super-scratchy!

Avoid grooming his ears and face with a dandy brush. The hard bristles are too rough for these sensitive places.

TECHNIQUE TIPS **Perfect your grooming technique with our top tips...**

● start grooming your pony at his neck and work your way to his hindquarters so you push dust and loose hair in one direction

● when grooming your pony's body, use a metal curry comb to clean hair out of your body brush. Use it every few strokes to stop your brush getting clogged up

● use the brush in your left hand and hold the curry comb in your right when grooming the left side of your pony, and hold the brush in your right hand and the curry comb in your left when grooming his right side

After grooming, flick off loose hairs with a long-bristled flick brush. These sweep hairs away, leaving your pony looking much tidier!

Gather up the hair your pony's shed and leave it out for the birds – they love to use it for their nests!

Turn him out with a friend – ponies enjoy mutual grooming and it often helps loosen stubborn hair around his withers.

SHED HIS COAT

Check out our top tips on how to help your pony get rid of his winter fluff

If the weather gives you a warm day, why not **treat your pony to a bath**? It'll remove loads more hair than grooming and get rid of grease, too.

Turn him out without his rug on when you can – he'll roll and get rid of lots of hair, which will save you some work.

Use a **body brush** quite firmly all over your pony's body to loosen and remove his moulting coat

FACT!

When ponies moult, they often roll more than usual, as the loosening hair makes them feel itchy and rolling is like a good scratch.

● stand close to your pony so you can bend your arms and get the most effective action

● use a body brush in sweeping motions using long strokes. This means the pressure of the strokes will be more even and help stimulate blood flow under his skin, resulting in a shinier coat

● spray a detangler into your pony's mane and tail before you groom them to loosen knots and make them easier to brush out

● when grooming your pony's tail, hold the hairs above where you're brushing them to reduce the risk of breaking the hairs

SUMMER SHOW SURPRISE

Ellie is super-excited about the arrival of her new pony, Tilly, and hopes to go to the village summer show. But will a twist in events stop them getting there?

Easter Sunday – the morning I went with Mum to pick up our new pony, Tilly – was probably the most excited I had been in months. I hadn't met Tilly before, but Mum had told me how gorgeous and sweet she was, so I couldn't wait to finally meet her. Mum had explained to me that Tilly's past owners hadn't been very caring and they had given her to Mum's friends, Paul and Barbara, when they got bored of looking after her. Barbara knew Mum was looking for a pony for us to share and thought that, after a bit of TLC, Tilly would be a perfect match. I was determined that Tilly would have a happy time with us and be able to forget about her past owners.

When we arrived at Paul and Barbara's house, I rushed straight to the stables to see if I could find Tilly. All the stables were empty apart from one, which had a bay mare in it, so I knew it must be her. Mum was right, although Tilly was still a little on the skinny side, she was beautiful! When the grown-ups had finished chatting about Tilly's progress, we loaded her into our trailer (she loaded like a pro) and took her home.

A new start

Over the next few weeks, Tilly settled in really well. She put on weight and started to look really shiny, especially as she'd begun to lose her winter coat. Mum did a bit of ridden work with her, mostly some quiet hacks, as she said it was important not to rush Tilly. It would be my turn soon and I couldn't wait to try jumping Tilly, but I knew that was still a few weeks away yet. I didn't mind waiting because I wanted everything to be perfect for Tilly.

I wanted all my friends to be just as excited about our new pony as I was, so I invited two of my friends from school, Abi and Liv, to come and meet her. But when they arrived and saw Tilly, they didn't react as I'd expected.

"She *is* pretty, Ellie, but she's a bit of an... errr... odd shape," said Liv. "It's a bit like she's fat and skinny at the same time. I can't quite work it out." Abi could tell that I was a bit upset by what Liv had said and she quickly added. "I'm sure you're going to do great together, Ellie. The summer show isn't for another

few months yet anyway, so you've got plenty of time to get her just perfect!" I replied and tried to smile: "Thanks Abi, I really hope so."

After Abi and Liv had gone, Mum could tell something was up. "What's wrong, Ellie? I thought you would be excited for Abi and Liv to meet Tilly?" I looked down at my hands. "I was, until Liv said Tilly looked

> **I wanted all my friends to be just as excited about our new pony as I was**

weird. She said she was fat in some places and skinny in others. Is Tilly okay?"

Mum paused, then said: "Well, to tell you the truth, Ellie, I've been starting to think the same myself." I was shocked that Mum could think something so mean about our beautiful pony. But she explained: "I've been trying to get her to put on a bit of weight, which she's been doing, but she's been putting it on in strange places. She doesn't look in any better condition, she's just been getting bigger and bigger. She just looks... pregnant." Now I was even more shocked. "Pregnant?! Tilly can't be pregnant! We're going to the summer show!" I exclaimed.

Mum explained that actually, although she couldn't be completely sure, it was possible that Tilly was in foal because we didn't really know much about what had happened to her before she arrived at Paul and Barbara's. Mum also explained how Tilly had been a bit grumpy when she had ridden her. But Mum had hoped it was just a phase. "I tried to make myself believe it wasn't possible, but a few days ago I was sure I saw her belly move. I thought I was seeing things because I haven't seen it move since. And I didn't say anything to you in case you got excited and it was a false alarm – which it still might be, Ellie, so try not to panic yourself just yet."

The big reveal

A few days later, our vet, David, came to see if he could confirm our suspicions. As soon as I brought Tilly out of her stable I could see David starting to smile, even though I could tell he was trying to hide it. He performed a rectal exam on Tilly, where he put his arm inside Tilly's bottom to feel around for a foal (so weird but so cool!).

Mum was doing a really good job of keeping her cool. I, on the other hand, felt like I was about to explode. I couldn't wait a minute longer to find out. I had stopped worrying about going to the summer show, because this was suddenly a lot more exciting.

"Sooooo?!" I asked David.

"Well I can't say 100%, but I think it's likely you got a two-for-one deal here when you got Tilly! I'll take some blood to confirm and it'll take a week before you get the result." I suddenly lost all hope of keeping my cool and practically jumped on Mum with excitement. I did at least manage to hold back from hugging David – that would have been mega cringeworthy! Mum and David talked about the practical things to do with the arrival of a foal, but I got straight on the phone to Abi and Liv – they would definitely be excited now!

About a week later, just as I got home from school, I heard Mum on the phone in the kitchen and she gave me a big thumbs up. "So how long have we got?" Mum asked and waited for a response. "Oh, I see. Well I guess it will just have to be a surprise then!" When she hung up, Mum explained that, because we didn't know how long Tilly had been pregnant for, David couldn't be sure when the foal was due. It was just a waiting game until he or she arrived.

Practising my patience

Over the next few weeks, there wasn't much we could do but keep a close eye on Tilly. David told us what signs to look for, but he also said that every mare is different, so we still wouldn't know exactly how quickly it was coming once we saw the signs. Mum and I started to think about what it would be like when the foal came. We had no idea whether it would be a filly or a colt, or what it would look like as we had no idea who the dad was. This made the waiting even more intense. I was kind of hoping for a palomino with four white socks, although Mum said that was pretty unlikely.

Every day before I went to school I got up extra-early to run out and check Tilly in the field before breakfast.

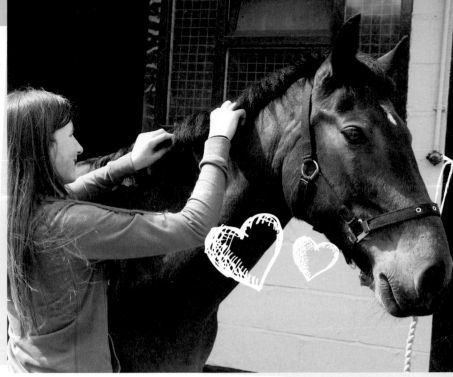

I knew Mum would be keeping an eye out in the day, but I checked her again as soon as I got home, and after dinner, and again just before I went to bed. I wanted to get up in the night and check, too, but when I suggested this to Mum she wouldn't even entertain the idea.

A few weeks later, I was still checking Tilly at every spare moment, but had given up getting up extra-early – six o'clock in the morning was the last thing I wanted to see when this foal just didn't seem to be appearing, especially on a weekend.

The next Saturday, I dragged myself outside to see Tilly at about 8 o'clock. Normally she would be waiting at the gate for her breakfast, especially as I was late, but she wasn't. I couldn't see her at first, so had to walk all the way round behind the trees on the right to search for her. How annoying, I thought.

As I rounded the corner, I couldn't believe my eyes – there was Tilly and she wasn't alone! Lying next to her was the cutest foal I'd ever seen (not that I'd seen many). I just knew this one was special. He had a spotty blanket bottom and, of all the foals I'd been imagining, I hadn't imagined markings as cool as this! I turned around to see Mum crossing the field with the biggest smile on her face.

"Looks like we might be going to the summer show after all, he's a looker! We can do some mare and foal classes together," Mum suggested. "What do you think to calling him Magic?" she continued. "He was a bit of a magical surprise, after all, wasn't he?"

This was the icing on the cake. I was so excited and couldn't wait to tell all my friends about Magic, and to make it even better, I was going to be able to show him and Tilly off at the summer show!

Make!
PLAITED BROWBANDS

Make your own browbands to match your cross-country colours or as a pretty present for your fave pony!

How to do it!

Step 1
Cut a piece of each ribbon colour double the length of your browband. Don't worry if the ribbon is a bit long, as you can trim it down later.

TOP TIP: Make sure you cut your ribbon diagonally or in a V shape at the ends, as this will stop them fraying.

Step 2
Line up the two pieces of ribbon, one on top of the other. Then, using the safety pin, fasten the two pieces of ribbon together about 2cm from the end. **You might need to ask an adult to help pin the ribbons.**

Step 3
Take the browband and place it between the two ribbons at the joined end, with one behind and one in front of the browband.

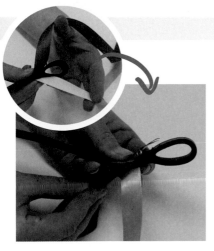

Step 4
Take the piece of ribbon nearest to you (the pink ribbon) and fold it over the browband away from you.

Step 5
Holding the pink ribbon in place, take the gold ribbon and fold it over the browband towards you, making sure it covers half of the first colour to form a triangle.

Step 6
Repeat the fold with the first colour again, making sure the ribbons cross over each other.

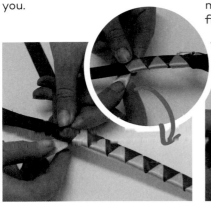

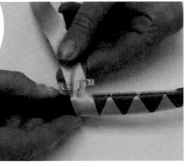

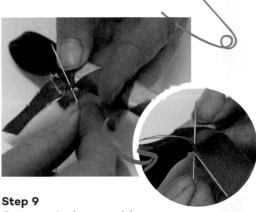

Step 7
Continue down the browband, folding each ribbon over in turn.

TOP TIP: Make sure you keep the ribbon flat on both sides, so it's comfortable for your pony to wear.

Step 8
Once you reach the end of the browband, pin the two pieces of ribbon together. Make sure that the ribbons finish on the same side so that they hang in the same direction.

Step 9
Once you're happy with your browband, take your needle and thread, and stitch the ribbons together at both ends. Stitch as close to the leather as you're able to. This will keep the ribbon tight and keep it looking neat. **Ask an adult for help with sewing if you're unsure**.

Step 10
Remove the safety pins and trim any excess ribbon so the ends are the same length. Your browband is now ready for your pony to wear.

Step 11
You can add sparkles to your browband by using stick-on gems if you like a bit of bling or leave it plain.

STEP 11

hand made

BREEDS
>> AKHAL-TEKE

The golden horse of the desert

> HISTORY

This elegant breed from Turkmenistan is known for its speed, stamina and intelligence. Because they're bred in a harsh desert climate, they're also super-hardy.

No one is quite sure about the origins of the breed because there aren't any written records, but it's possible that breeds such as the Arabian, Turkoman, Akhal-Teke and Barb all share a single ancestor.

Tribal people in what is now Turkmenistan first used the Akhal-Teke for raiding other tribes and their horses were their most treasured possessions. Before raids, the horses were put on a sparse diet to prepare them for the long ride through the desert with no water and hardly any feed. Their owners admired their speed and stamina in the desert, and their loyalty.

> STANDARDS

Akhal-Tekes are usually between 14.2 and 16hh. They have a delicate head with a straight nose that's sometimes slightly dished, a bit like an Arabian, and long ears. Their manes and tails are fine and silky, their necks are quite upright, and their backs long and muscular.

Akhal-Tekes are good gallopers!

COOL COAT

The coat of Akhal-Teke horses has a beautiful metallic sheen, thanks to the structure of the hair. Rather than being opaque, like most horse hair, Akhal-Tekes have much more translucent hair, which creates a sparkly glow.

As well as unusual colours, such as buckskin, perlino and palomino, you can find black, bay, chestnut and grey Akhal-Tekes. They often have blue eyes, too.

HIGHLY DECORATED

The Turkmen people had jewellers called zergers who made beautiful, decorated harnesses for the royal Akhal-Teke horses. These harnesses were made from gold, silver and bronze, and were decorated with precious stones. People in Turkmenistan still make the traditional tack, although they now use nickel and brass instead of super-expensive silver and gold. The harnesses are decorated with coloured glass and even semi-precious stones such as carnelians.

WOOL COLLARS

The Turkmen people are very superstitious and often decorate their horses with wool collars called alajas to protect them. The collars are made from dyed, braided camel or sheep wool that's decorated with beads and charms, and sometimes even precious stones. The more elaborate alajas are often given as prizes to winning jockeys.

WHAT CAN THEY DO?

Akhal-Tekes make good sport horses and have been known to excel in dressage, showjumping, eventing, racing and endurance riding. An Akhal-Teke stallion named Absent even won the Grand Prix de Dressage at the 1960 Rome Olympics.

FUN FACT!
The Akhal-Teke is featured on the coat of arms, banknotes and stamps of Turkmenistan. They're the country's national emblem.

GIVE *showjumping* A GO!

Showjumping is loads of fun and the best part is that you can enjoy it all year round!

If you and your fave pony have been flying over fences in your lessons, you might be thinking about entering your first show. It's important to know what to expect, so have a look at our guide to getting started in showjumping.

Fence guide

There are lots of different types of fence on a showjumping course. Here's the low-down on what you might be asked to jump.

TOP TIP

Remember to stay positive – if *you* don't think you can do it, your pony won't, either.

OXERS

An oxer, also known as a spread, is made up of two verticals placed slightly apart from one another. This means that your pony must stretch over the fence to clear both poles. An oxer can be ascending – lower on the take-off side and higher at the back – or parallel, with both poles set at the same height.

To clear an oxer in style, ask your pony to open up his canter a little by squeezing him with your legs and keeping him balanced with your hands. Your pony will find oxers easier and more fun to fly over from this more forward canter!

VERTICALS

Verticals are pretty straightforward fences and you've probably jumped loads of them! A vertical is an upright jump consisting of poles and maybe fillers, and requires your pony to jump upwards in a smooth, round shape.

Some ponies can be a bit lazy over verticals, so before you approach them, make sure your canter is balanced with a short, active stride. You want your pony to feel a bit like a bouncy ball – this means that when he gets to the fence he can pop over it easily.

RELATED DISTANCES

A related distance is made up of two fences that are more than two strides, but less than six strides, apart. These fences can be set on a straight line or on a slight bend, known as a dog-leg. It's important to make a plan for any related distances you see when you're walking a course. For example, if you have an oxer with five strides to a vertical, you know that you have five strides to get your pony into that 'bouncy ball' canter before the vertical.

> **IT'S IMPORTANT TO MAKE A PLAN FOR ANY RELATED DISTANCES YOU SEE WHEN YOU'RE WALKING A COURSE**

DOUBLES

A double is two fences in a row, with one or two canter strides between them. These fences can be verticals or oxers.

The two most important things to remember when jumping a double are straightness and impulsion. Plan your line into the double nice and early – no cutting in tight here! Keep your eyes on the middle of the second fence as you approach the first, then look up and ahead as you land!

If you find your pony has an awkward jump at the first element, don't take your leg off as you land – sit up and squeeze your pony forwards to keep the impulsion and a straight line over the second element.

TOP TIP

Always look ahead to your next fence to keep your pony thinking forward – and to help you remember where you're going!

Competition day!

There's lots to see and hear at a show, so you might find your pony has a bit more get-up-and-go than usual! Bring a haynet for him to munch on so he feels at home while you walk the course and collect your number.

Walking the course

When you're walking the course, make sure to walk the lines between the fences just as you plan to ride them – don't cut corners! Count the strides in combinations and related distances so that you can get to the perfect take-off point every time.

To work out your distances, take three big steps – that's one pony stride. Make sure to add half a pony stride (one-and-a-half of your steps) for both landing and take-off – so if you can fit six big steps between two jumps, there's one canter stride between them.

TOP TIP

Give yourself plenty of time at the show to walk your course – you're allowed to walk it as many times as you need to, so take your time and really learn it!

Warming up

Before you ride the course, you need to make sure your pony is properly warmed up and listening to you. Warm-up rings usually have two fences – a cross-pole or vertical and an oxer.

Check which way you should be jumping the fences to avoid crashing into other competitors! There will normally be a red flag or wing on the right and a white flag or wing on the left.

If it's busy, it's a good idea to let others know when you're approaching the jump – for example, call out 'oxer' or 'vertical', so people in the ring know what you're planning to jump and can stay out of your way.

TOP TIP

Practise balanced transitions in your warm-up to get a really good showjumping canter. Going from trot to canter and back to trot again a few times will get your pony listening to you.

TOP TIP

Remember to always pass left-to-left in the warm-up arena and pay attention to where other competitors are at all times – never cross behind or in front of a fence.

RIDING A COURSE

Riding a whole course gives you a lot more to think about than riding a single fence! The bits between the jumps are just as important as the jumps themselves, so make sure you stay focused and think about your plan the whole way around.

If your pony starts to rush around the course, he's more likely to knock poles, so half-halt him between fences by wrapping your legs around his sides and closing your hands on the reins to contain his energy, then releasing your hands. This will shift his energy to his quarters and get him balanced again.

If you have a run-out or a refusal, stay calm and ride a circle to build up a steady trot or canter. Encourage your pony to jump the middle of the fence by hugging him with your legs and seat, and keeping an even contact on both reins.

AND REMEMBER...
Have fun! The best thing about showjumping is that there are always lots of opportunities to try again if it doesn't go to plan.

DID YOU KNOW?

The full ceremonial kit a horse carries weighs about 25kg – plus the weight of a person!

Soldiers in the Household Cavalry don't just take part in ceremonial duties – they're all fully trained soldiers who fight for their country, too.

Post Card

Summer hols!
Every summer, all the horses and riders head to Norfolk for four weeks as part of their annual training. The horses get the chance to have a dip in the sea and a break from London life.

PLACE
STAMP
HERE

Holkham Beach,
Norfolk

Handsome horses

All the horses in the Household Cavalry are known as Cavalry Blacks for their jet black coats. The only exceptions are the drum horses and the grey horses ridden by the trumpeters.

Horses are bought at around three or four years old. They're ready to begin work after a year of training, once they're used to large crowds, heavy traffic and loud noises.

The average age of retirement for the horses is 17–18 years old, with some making it into their twenties.

Look sharp!

For day-to-day exercise, the horses wear brown tack, but for public duties they're decked-out in their super-smart black tack. This ceremonial kit takes around three hours of checking and polishing to make sure it's up to the job – yikes!

CHIVALROUS HOUSEHOLD CAVALRY

There's nothing more impressive than the sight of super-smart horses and riders parading through the capital city

DAILY DUTIES

The Household Cavalry provides a daily guard, called the Queen's Life Guard, outside the ceremonial entrance to Buckingham Palace. They also act as an escort to The Queen and other visiting heads of state, and carry out a number of ceremonial duties throughout the year, including The Queen's birthday parade and Royal weddings.

Drum horses

Drum horses are gorgeous heavy horses, and they carry the huge metal drums that are used during processions and ceremonies. The drums each weigh more than 30kg and the horses carry two of these, along with ceremonial kit and a rider!

As the riders use their hands to play the drums, they control the horses through reins that attach to their stirrups.

Musical rides

The Musical Ride of the Household Cavalry has been performed at county shows since the 1880s, and shows off the skills the horses and riders would need in war. One of the most impressive skills is teaching their horses to lie down and stay down on command.

WHAT'S YOUR PONY'S PERSONALITY?

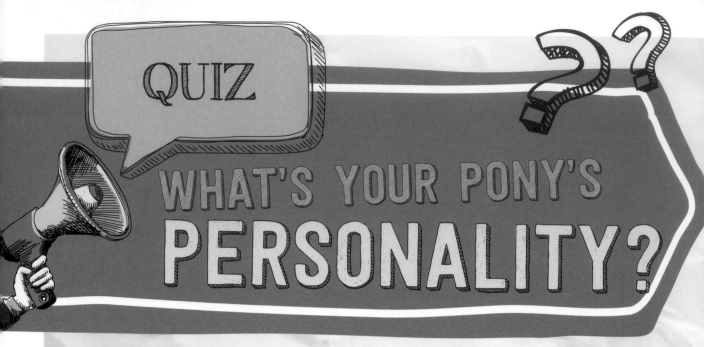

Is your fave pony a cool customer or a drama queen?
Or how about a speed merchant or a nosy parker?
Take our quiz to find out!

Cool customer

1. You're out on a hack on a summer's day. Does your pony...

A ...throw his head up and jog trot. He can't wait to gallop.

B ...look up all the paths and in the hedges, checking for monsters.

M WTR C ...walk along on a long rein enjoying the change from the school.

Z D ...refuse to go through muddy puddles and get his hooves dirty.

2. You're heading off to a show so you give your fave pony a bath. How does he react?

RTW A He won't stand still and can't believe you're trying to get him wet!

B He looks worried – shows make him nervous.

C He gets super-excited. Baths mean fun things.

DZM D He enjoys the attention he's getting. It's soooo relaxing.

3. You've got a dressage competition coming up and you need to have a serious schooling session. What are your pony's thoughts?

R A Flatwork is sooo boring! Let's jump instead.

D B How can you expect me to work with so much to look at? I've got to see what the other horse in here is doing!

TMW C Come on, let's get this done.

Z D I've not been in here for a week, the monsters have probably moved back. I've got to check everywhere before I can work.

4. How does your pony react to a visit from the farrier?

A He stands quietly. After all, the quieter he stands, the sooner he can go back to eating grass.

T B He paws the ground impatiently.

MD C He nuzzles the farrier, looking for treats.

MW D He's very fidgety and seems suspicious of what the farrier is doing.

5. You're riding a cross-country course. How does it go?

A) Your pony's a bit reluctant, but it's okay until you reach the water jump – then it's game over!

B) You always go clear, your pony's an amazing jumper and he never stops.

C) Good, but you could have done with better brakes!

D) It's okay once you get him to concentrate and listen to you.

E) No jumping (DQ)

6. You're having a dressage lesson somewhere new. How does your pony behave?

A) If it's not jumping, he's not really interested. He doesn't have the patience for this dressage stuff.

B) It's your pony's time to shine. He loves strutting his stuff and showing off.

C) He's super-excited, there's so much to see. He loves going to new places.

D) He's calm. He behaves the same way he would if he was at home.

nervous - eek (DQ)

7. You've been on holiday so haven't ridden in a while. When you get back on your pony, how does he react?

A) He's excited to be ridden again, which means he's super-speedy!

B) He's obviously forgotten what the arena looks like and decides to spook in every corner.

C) He's enjoyed his time off and tries his best to let you know he needs more holiday by throwing in a few cheeky bucks.

D) He's the same as always and is happy to be back in work.

8. You're on a hack with a friend and decide to have a canter up a grassy hill. What does your pony think?

A) He's too busy looking at the scenery to listen to your aids. He barely even realises your friend has started to canter!

B) It's a race and he's got to win!

C) He's up for it and is happy to go in front or behind, steady or fast.

D) He's got to be in front. He can't possibly stay behind and get covered in dust or be ignored by the other pony.

don't wanna (DQ)

Speed merchant

9. It's tea time for your pony. What happens?

A) If he doesn't get fed now, he's going to starve! Or at least bang his stable door.

B) He happily waits for his feed. He knows he's going to be fed, so why worry?

C) He looks over the door between mouthfuls to check on everyone else.

D) You've got to make his feed a bit sloppy so it takes him longer to eat, or he'll bolt it.

E) never in at night

10. You're leading your pony in from the field. How does he behave?

A) He tries to rifle through your pockets. He knows you've got more treats somewhere!

B) He tries to trot to the yard, he's super excited, he might get to go for a ride.

C) He walks next to you, but swerves around puddles – he can't get his hooves dirty!

D) He walks calmly by your side.

11. You've made it to the jump-off at a competition. Your pony is…

A) …super-fast and careful. You've totally got this!

B) …fab! He loves being in the ring and being the centre of attention.

C) …too busy watching everything going on around him, he's not concentrating so he's likely to have a pole down.

D) …likely to go clear and you might be fast enough, especially if you ride some tight angles.

E) No jumping (DQ)

12. You're a little late to the yard in the morning. How does your pony react?

A) He won't come and say hello, as you'd clearly forgotten all about him.

B) He's walking around his stable, eager to be turned out.

C) He's still waiting patiently for you to arrive.

D) He doesn't really mind, as he's enjoyed watching other ponies coming and going.

I'm a lazy parker

Drama queen

Turn to page 100 to work out your score and discover your pony's personality!

A WHOLE NEW WORLD

When Milly visited her pony, Scottie, late one evening she couldn't believe what she saw...

I've often heard that if a pony is found sweaty in his stable in the morning, then he's been ridden by a witch during the night. This obviously isn't true but, like all myths, I think it began with some element of truth that got lost along the way. Not many people really know the truth – but I do. I've seen ponies disappear from their stables and return in the morning hot and blowing. And I've seen the creatures that take them.

It all started with an argument with my parents one summers' evening. They wanted me to spend less time with Scottie, my totally awesome grey pony, and more time on my school work. They didn't think my dream of becoming a professional event rider could be a reality. I wanted to be like Pippa Funnell and they wanted me to be the next Einstein. I ran out of the house with Dad's voice trailing behind me: "We haven't finished this conversation, Milly!"

I just needed to escape to my favourite place in the world – Scottie's stable. The livery yard was at the end of our lane so I arrived quickly, knowing my parents wouldn't bother to come looking for me as they'd guess where I'd gone. We'd had the same argument time and time again. They knew I'd be back in my room in a few hours, ignoring them until the morning. I quietly let myself into Scottie's stable. He looked up from munching his hay as I put my arms around his neck and sobbed into his mane.

"Why don't they understand I only want to ride, Scottie? They don't believe in us. They don't think we can make it!" I whispered. Scottie snorted, showing he understood and agreed with me. He was an amazing pony. He could jump anything and rarely got any faults showjumping. He loved to go cross-country, too, and although neither of us particularly enjoyed dressage, we usually did okay. Soon I ran out of tears, but rather than trudging home as usual, I decided to stay and chat to Scottie for a little while.

The magic begins

The sound of excited whinnies startled me – I'd fallen asleep. It was dark outside Scottie's stable. Once my eyes adjusted to the gloom, I realised I'd been here longer than I'd planned, and a glance at my phone showed it was midnight. I panicked and quickly got up and walked to the door, turning to say goodbye to Scottie. I noticed he was alert, standing tall, staring expectantly at the centre of the yard.

"Strange..." I thought. "...I wonder if there's a fox or badger out there?" Turning to look, what I saw instead stunned me. An eerie green, glowing ball had appeared in the middle of the yard. Scottie snorted and stamped the ground, gazing at the ball of light. As I watched, the ball expanded, growing brighter until it was blinding and the size of a small horsebox.

A small figure appeared from the middle of the ball and darted forwards, unbolting and opening all the stable doors. I watched in amazement and shock as all the ponies on the yard trotted excitedly into the green light and disappeared. Scottie was the last to be let out and he turned to look at me before stepping through the light, as it began to shrink again.

I didn't hesitate and sprinted for the light, jumping through after the horses. I had to find out where they were going and who'd taken my pony!

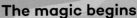

> " The sound of excited whinnies startled me – I'd fallen asleep "

A strange new world

The light surrounded me, making my skin glow a bright, emerald green and ahead I could just see a faint, white glow and the silhouette of one of the ponies. I quickly followed, not wanting to be trapped alone in the green tunnel. Stepping out, I found myself in the most beautiful place I'd ever seen. I couldn't believe how green it was. There was soft, dewy grass, sprinkled with thousands of flowers in every colour. The sky had two suns and bright blue, fluffy clouds, I was awestruck. In the distance I could see a cloud of moving dust as the ponies cantered around in excitement.

Just then, I heard a soft nicker and turned to see Scottie waiting for me. He was standing next to an old tree stump and kept looking between me and his back. I understood that he wanted me to ride him, so I jumped onto the tree stump and mounted. Scottie let me get settled and take hold of his mane before setting off at a canter. As we flew through the meadow, I noticed other groups of horses and ponies of all shapes and sizes, most of which I'd never seen before, hurrying in the same direction. A few of them whinnied in greeting to Scottie, who nickered in reply. Some cantered alongside us as we continued towards what looked like a big crater.

All of the horses slowed as we came to the edge. Scottie dropped back to a trot, turning to follow the edge of the crater. As I looked down the steep slope that descended into the middle, I saw horses and ponies everywhere – small Welsh ponies, Shire horses, smart Thoroughbreds and scruffy Shetlands to name a few. I stared in disbelief. I'd never seen so many equines in one place! It was a stunning sight. Scottie joined the mass of ponies making their way down into the crater. Once we reached the centre, he stood still, waiting for me to dismount. Once I was back on the ground, he gently nuzzled me with his head before taking off into the crowd.

The gate keeper

I suddenly felt very alone and lost, surrounded by all these ponies I didn't know. Glancing around, I decided I'd try to make my way to a small lake in the distance, but trying to navigate around all the gathered ponies wasn't easy. After trying a few different routes, I eventually reached the lake. Hundreds of ponies were playing in the water – splashing, rolling and galloping ➤

through it. I was so busy watching and laughing at their antics that I didn't notice a small person approaching me.

"Excuse me," said a small, squeaky voice, "who are you and what are you doing here?" Startled, I jumped and looked down to see the same figure who'd let the ponies out at the yard. She was only about 50cm tall with long, blue hair that reached the middle of her back and fiery, red eyes. I thought she might be a pixie. She looked up at me, puzzled.

"I'm Milly," I stuttered. "I came here with my pony, Scottie. I don't know where he's gone, he dropped me off in the crater and went off. Where am I? What is this place? Why did you let all the ponies out at the yard? Who are you?" I had a million more questions whizzing around my head.

"I'm Safire, or Saf if you prefer. This world is called Wallen. It's the place where the horses and ponies of Earth come for a holiday. They can spend a whole Earth night here playing and meeting other equines. I'm the keeper of Wallen, I control who enters and leaves. All the ponies here have proven they're kind, hard-working and won't cause trouble. This is a place of peace and trouble-makers aren't allowed!" She explained. "You're the first human to enter this world." Safire smiled at me, but continued: "I'm afraid you'll have to leave with your pony and you can't return here. It's a place for the horses and ponies to be free for a few hours."

"I understand, but I'm not sure how I'm going to find Scottie. There are thousands of ponies here. How do they know when it's time to go home?" I asked.

"Scottie will find you. There's magic in Wallen. Horses and ponies can use telepathy, so he'll track you through his connection to you – call for him now and he'll come. As for how they know it's time to go home,

" *Scottie will find you. There is magic in Wallen* **"**

we have opposite nights and days to Earth. Once our suns begin to set, the ponies start to make the journey back to the gate that brought them here."

"That's amazing! Do ponies possess any other magical abilities? Do I have any magical abilities here?" I almost shouted at Safire, eager to find out more information.

"Other than the telepathic link with Scottie, I'm not sure. You're the first human I've met." Safire started to look concerned. "I'm afraid we're running out of time – the suns are beginning to set, so you must find Scottie and go home." Saf began searching the crowd of ponies as she finished speaking. "Call to him with your mind and he'll come. I must go, I've got to keep the gate open until the last pony leaves – I'm sorry. Have a safe journey back. Remember, you can't come here again." With these parting words, Saf disappeared into the mass of equines.

Returning home

Remembering her warning, I crossed my fingers and called in my head for Scottie, then closed my eyes and hoped. When I opened them I saw Scottie trotting towards me. A nearby rock helped me mount and we were off again. This time it was no steady canter, but a flat-out gallop! We had to race the sunset. The wind rushed past my face as we flew across the landscape. We continued to gallop straight through the gate and I waved at Safire as we zoomed past, but Scottie was going too fast for me to see if she waved back.

By the time we made it back to the yard, Scottie was dripping with sweat. We turned to watch as the last pony came through the portal and, with a soft pop, the green light vanished. Scottie and I stood still for a minute to let our eyes adjust to the early morning light before I slid from his back and led him back to his stable. After making sure the other ponies were back and safely bolted in, I made my way back home, crept upstairs and got straight into bed. I knew no one would believe my incredible story, but at least now I know what ponies really get up to when we think they're asleep!

10 ways to show your pony YOU LOVE HIM

We all love ponies – that's a no-brainer – but how can you show your fave pony you love him without smothering him? Try our top 10 ideas and you'll be his fave person in no time!

1 GO GRAZING

If your fave pony spends lots of time in his stable, why not hand graze him? Pop his headcollar on and take him to a patch of juicy grass where he can have a munch. He'll enjoy the change of scenery and you'll get to spend some quality time with him, too.

2 GET CRAFTY

Ponies love treats – fact! Spoil him by making some yummy pony snacks. Look up recipes online to find something your pony will love!

3 KEEP HIM BUSY

Just like us, ponies don't like to be bored. Bust boredom by varying his ridden routine. Mix up schooling, hacking and jumping to keep him interested. Make sure he's occupied in his stable, too, by giving him toys such as a treat ball, or try chopping up apples and carrots and hiding them in his haynet.

4 SUPER SCRATCH

Ponies like to spend time grooming each other in the field, so when he's not turned out, give him a good scratch on all his itchy spots. On his withers and behind his ears are common fave spots.

5 PONY SPA DAY

Treat your pony to a spa day and makeover! Wait for a hot day, then give him a full bath. Not only will he look super-shiny and smart, it'll also help him loosen any shedding coat if he's moulting, which will make him feel less itchy. After a bath, neaten up his mane by pulling or thinning it and give his tail a trim. You'll both enjoy the results!

6 KEEP IT CLEAN

Give your pony's tack a thorough clean and wash his numnah to keep him feeling comfy when you ride him. Brush excess hair from the inside of his rugs, too.

7 SPRUCE UP HIS STABLE

Give your pony's stable some extra attention – it's his bedroom after all! Start by using a fork to move all the bedding up into banks so the stable floor is exposed to allow it to dry thoroughly. Leave it for the day, then pull it back down into a comfy bed. Remove any cobwebs from around his stable, too.

8 PONY MASSAGE

Pamper your pony with a massage. After a ride, gently massage him along his neck and back by moving your fingers in small circles. He'll find it mega-relaxing and it'll strengthen your bond, too!

9 DO SOMETHING HE LOVES

Every pony has a fave activity – a long canter out hacking, cross-country schooling or playing mounted games in the arena. Whatever it is, treat your pony to a bit of what he loves doing.

10 QUALITY DOWN TIME

Ponies love down time for some proper rest and relaxation. Leave him be in his stable to have a snooze or turn him out in the field to graze with his mates. After all, a relaxed pony is a happy pony!

High Kingdom

PONY brings you the inside scoop on this royal horse!

Stable name: Trev • Discipline: Eventing
Ridden by: Zara Tindall

after his owner, Trevor Hemmings!

High Kingdom was born in 2001 in County Wicklow, Ireland, at the farm of famed horse breeder and trainer, William Micklem. His dam, High Dolly, evented to Intermediate level and his sire is the famous eventing stallion, Master Imp, so there was never any doubt in William's mind that he had bred a future champion!

It took Trev a while to grow into himself, though. For the first few years of his life, he was a bit of an ugly duckling and always looked lanky and younger than he was. He didn't have a naturally good trot and he took a long time to learn how to move well under saddle. His jumping, however, was always brilliant – from a young age he would jump from field to field for fun, and his natural balance was so good that he was nearly sold as a showjumper.

Climbing the levels
Zara took up the reins in 2007, after having only seen photos and video of Trev. The handsome bay said goodbye to the herd of youngsters he'd been living with in Ireland and made the journey to Zara's yard in England.

Zara loved Trev right away, and his natural talent and fab personality meant that they enjoyed loads of success in Trev's first year of competition.

His favourite phase is cross-country, as he's a bit of an adrenalin junkie and loves to go fast and jump!

Yard life
Trev definitely knows the difference between his working time and his well-earned time off! While he loves to compete and has a great attitude, he really enjoys coming home from an event and going out in the field.

He's a very chilled-out boy, but isn't keen on a fuss – he much prefers to be left alone to enjoy a big feed or a good graze! His groom has to keep a close eye on him, though – he still enjoys practising his jumping over the fences around Zara's yard!

Famous family
Trev's sire, Master Imp, is considered one of the best eventing sires in the world. As a result, international competition tends to be a family affair! Trev competed against three of his half-siblings at the London Olympics – Master Crusoe (Ireland), Master Rose (Ecuador) and Ringwood Magister (USA).

His full brother, Mandiba, competed at the 2008 Beijing Olympics for the United States with top eventer, Karen O'Connor.

He's also related to showjumper Kilbaha, who won the Hickstead Derby in 1994 and 1995 – must be where that showjumping talent comes from!

DID YOU KNOW?
Zara has described Trev as being like a pony to ride – the 16.1hh gelding is so balanced and bouncy that he doesn't feel like a horse!

LIKES

- meal-times – he's very fond of his food!
- apples and carrots
- a good adrenalin rush – he likes nothing more than to gallop and jump
- his best horsey mate, Watkins

DISLIKES

- too much fuss – he prefers to be left alone
- staying in his own field!

DREAM COME TRUE

Trev took Zara to her first Olympics, something she had been dreaming of for years. She had been selected for the team twice before with Toytown, in 2004 and 2008, but had to withdraw both times because of injury.

TOP RESULTS

2014 World Equestrian Games – team silver, 11th individually
2013 Luhmühlen Horse Trials – 2nd
2012 London Olympics – team silver, 8th individually
2011 Burghley Horse Trials – 10th

DID YOU KNOW?

Trev is a fast learner – he went from competing in 90cm classes to his first CCI** in less than a year!

Competing at the World Equestrian Games

BRED TO EVENT

Just like High Kingdom, rider Zara Tindall also has famous eventing parents. Her mum, Princess Anne, competed at two European Championships and went to the 1976 Olympics. Her dad, Captain Mark Phillips, won European, World and Olympic medals.

Show off!

We all want to show off our ponies, and have everyone else love and admire them as much as we do. So why not have a go at showing? Follow PONY's fab guide for all you need to know

Showing is where riders and their ponies compete against each other in a class with specific criteria. Some popular classes include Pony Club Pony, Best Turned Out, Family Pony and Pony the Judge Would Most Like to Take Home. There are classes based on your pony's breed, type or colour – for example, Cob Type, Mountain and Moorland, Coloured and Working Hunter Pony.

Showing can be ridden or in-hand, and the winner and placings are chosen by a showing judge. You can take part in showing at many levels, from local and Pony Club shows to national and international competitions. Rules and regulations vary at each level, so make sure you check them before entering.

Choosing a class

Certain classes will suit some rider and pony combinations more than others. Take into account your pony's breed, height and colour, as well as your strengths and weaknesses as a combination. If you aren't a confident jumper, avoid classes that require you to jump, such as Pony Club Pony. Instead, pick something that doesn't involve jumping – for example, Condition and Turnout.

Don't be tempted to enter classes that aren't suited to you and your pony – for example, if your pony is a New Forest, don't enter a class for cob types – you'll only be disappointed when you don't do very well!

TRICKS OF THE TRADE

Showing regulars and professionals know that the details matter and often use grooming tricks to make their ponies stand out in the crowd. Here's a few to try...

● **Chalk** Applying chalk to your pony's white points – for example, leg markings or face markings – will make them super-white and help your pony appear super-clean. Rub the chalk in, then go over it with a brush. Crafty!

● **Finishing cloth** These are designed to give your pony's coat a high shine, perfect for use just before you enter the show ring.

● **Baby oil** Applying baby oil to your pony's muzzle will make him gleam. Use a cloth to apply a very small amount, as lots can irritate your pony's nose. Also, be careful when using it on sunny days, as it can make your pony's skin more sensitive to the sun.

Preparation is key

Making sure you know what to expect on the day of the show and what you'll need to do in order to be well-prepared will make all the difference. Follow our essential preparation points to make sure you're ready to show off...

At home
✓ practise your individual show
✓ perfect your square halt
✓ bath and groom your pony the day before so he's spotless!
✓ make sure you have correct and clean tack
✓ pack a clean white, black or brown numnah (it's down to personal preference which your pony wears)
✓ plan your warm-up

At the show
✓ Remove any boots or bandages from your pony before you enter the ring
✓ Ask a friend to stand ring-side with a brush or finishing cloth, so they can give your pony a last-minute going-over before you enter the ring

➤

DID YOU KNOW?
Apply a black or clear varnish to your pony's feet (depending on the colour of your pony's hooves) instead of grease, as grease will attract dirt.

WHAT TO WEAR

Black or navy fixed peak hat, or a skull cap with black or navy cover

Hairnet or ribbons

Jacket - navy, black or tweed

Shirt and tie or stock and pin

Tweed jacket

Cream jodhpurs or breeches

Long leather boots, short boots and leather gaiters or short boots and jodhpur clips

DID YOU KNOW?

At shows, you might see ponies with different coloured ribbons in their tail. Red means the pony might kick, so should be given plenty of room. Green means the pony is young or inexperienced and yellow or blue means the pony is a stallion, so could be unpredictable in his behaviour. White means the pony is for sale.

WHAT TO EXPECT

Ridden

In ridden classes, you'll be asked to ride around the show ring together in walk and trot and, depending on the level of the show, usually canter, too. Once the judge has seen this you'll be called into a line up, where all competitors stand in a row alongside one another, then you'll each be asked to perform an individual show. Your individual show should include walk, trot and canter on both reins. Some classes will require you to jump a fence or show a short gallop, but the judge or steward will tell you if you need to do this.

In-hand

In an in-hand showing class, you'll be asked to lead your pony around the show ring in a line with the other competitors. You'll then be called into a line up, where you'll need to stand your pony up. This is where you ask him to halt and stand still so the judge can assess him. The correct place to stand is directly in front of your pony so you're facing each other. This way, you won't get in the way of the judge. You'll also be asked to walk and trot your pony away from and towards the judge.

RING CRAFT

Ring craft is the art of showing off your pony as well as you can.

Ridden

In order for you to show off your pony, you need to remember to ride as well as you can. Tidy and effective riding will give a much better overall picture than lazy or messy riding.

There are a few tricks you can use in the ring to help you give the best impression you can to the judge. First, make sure your pony is as relaxed as possible, but also moving forward with balanced paces. A well-behaved pony will almost always be placed higher than a pony who misbehaves, no matter how pretty or smart the naughty pony is!

Try not to make a transition right in front of the judge, as there's a risk it may not be as smooth as you'd like. Get your pony going nicely in whatever pace you're in before you ride past the judge. Remember, the judge will be looking all around the ring, so don't relax your riding once you've passed by. Ride as well as you can the whole time you're in the ring!

In-hand

It's important to make sure your pony's walk is purposeful and his trot is active – you don't want to look like you're dragging him along! Also, make sure you lead him in a straight line – the judge won't get an accurate view of how he moves if he's going from side-to-side or in a wonky line. Walk beside his shoulder to encourage him to keep moving forwards.

Clean bill of PONY HEALTH

Want to know if your fave pony is in tip-top form? Here's what you need to look for...

Standing

Your pony should be **standing evenly on all four feet**. If he's resting a hindleg, this is usually okay, but it's not normal to rest a front leg.

Eyes

His **eyes should be wide open and bright**, and he should be **alert and responsive** to things going on around him. If your pony's not feeling great, he might not have the energy to do this.

Behaviour

Your pony will have his own **normal way of behaving** and his own personality. If he suddenly starts behaving differently – for example, being really grumpy – he might not be feeling 100%.

Temperature

Your pony's **temperature should be 37.5–38.5°C** while he's resting. It will go up slightly when he's being ridden, but that's normal. You can take his temperature by gently pulling a thermometer into his bottom – remember to keep hold of the thermometer all the time and stand to one side of your pony, not directly behind him. If it reaches 39°C or more, then you need to call your vet.

Eating

When your pony's feeling great, **he'll eat all his food** and chew normally. If he becomes disinterested in his food, it could be because he's feeling poorly.

Sweating

Unless he's been exercising, **he shouldn't show any signs of sweating**. If you go into his stable and he looks sweaty, then this could be a sign that he's in pain.

Coat

His **coat should be shiny and lying flat**. A super-shiny coat shows you that his body has enough energy and nutrients to keep his coat in good condition.

➤

Pulse

His **pulse rate should be 35–45 beats per minute**. The easiest place to take it is under his jaw, but it still takes a bit of practice – ask your yard owner or vet to show you. It can go up quite quickly if he gets nervous or excited, but if it's more than 55 beats per minute while he's quiet with no distractions around, call your vet.

Eyelids, nostrils & gums

Take a close look at your pony's eyelids, nostrils and gums – they should be a **salmon pink** colour.

Breathing

Your pony should take **10–20 breaths each minute** while he's resting and these should be regular and take little effort. It's normal for this to increase quite quickly if he's excited, nervous or exercising. Stand at your pony's head, looking towards his bottom and count each time his belly expands with a big breath.

Legs

His **legs should be free from swellings and heat**. If any of them are puffy or warm, he might have picked up an injury.

Urine

Your pony's **urine should be either colourless or pale yellow** and passed several times a day. If it's a dark colour then he hasn't had enough to drink and is dehydrated.

Condition

He shouldn't be too fat or too thin, but in **good condition**. You should be able to feel his ribs, but not see them, and he shouldn't have a hard, cresty neck, or a gutter along his back or bottom.

Poo

Your pony should **poo around eight times a day**, depending on how much he's been eating. His poo should be like damp balls that break when they hit the ground. If your pony has just moved to a new field with more grass, his droppings might be a bit green and sloppy at first (yuk!) but after a few days, they should be back to normal.

Lameness

Your pony should **show no signs of lameness** and be able to move around freely. He should make steps of the same size with each leg and put equal amounts of weight through each foot.

It's really important that you get to know what's normal for your fave pony — every time you see him, make a mental note of how he is and soon you won't even have to think about it. When you get to the yard, give him a quick check over to make sure he's okay and, if anything isn't quite right, you'll pick it up quickly and be able to get him the help he needs. Don't panic if you do notice something odd about your pony because he won't always be exactly the same every day. But, if you're still worried, call your vet for some advice.

Make!

TOTALLY COOL
TACK TAGS

Accessorise your bridle and saddle with these jazzy tags so everyone can tell whose tack is whose, and to help keep your pony safe if you fall off

hand made

TOP TIP: Tack tags are really useful if you fall off on a hack (oops!) because, if someone finds your pony, they will have your contact details to ensure he's safely returned.

You will need...
- ☑ coloured paper, card or fabric
- ☑ scissors
- ☑ felt tip pens
- ☑ glue
- ☑ decorations
- ☑ laminator and a laminating sheet, or sticky back plastic
- ☑ hole punch
- ☑ metal key rings

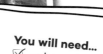

You don't have to make your tag a rectangle shape — use these cool examples to get creative!

How to do it!

Step 1
Draw your shape onto card – a bank card is a good size to draw around for a saddle tag and the end of a glue stick is perfect for a bridle tag, but you can do any shape you like.

Step 2
Write your pony's name and your emergency contact details on your saddle tag using a felt tip pen, and your pony's name on your bridle tag.

TOP TIP: Make sure you include the name and address of your yard, and an emergency contact number of someone there, just in case you fall off and lose your pony. If you don't have enough room, you can always write it on the back.

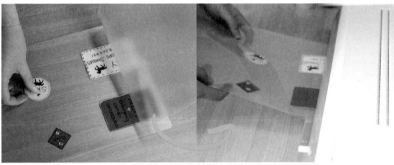

Step 3
Decorate your tags with anything you like. You could use glitter, sequins or paint.

Step 4
Ask an adult to help you laminate your tags when the decorations are dry. If you don't have a laminator, you could use clear, sticky back plastic to keep them protected.

Step 5
Cut around your laminated tags, leaving a 1/2cm border.

Step 6
Punch a hole through the top of your tags and attach them to your tack using metal key rings. If you don't have a key ring, you could use matching string, but make sure it's secure!

BREEDS

>> MUSTANGS

America's most famous breed

> HISTORY

The wild horses that roamed across the North American grasslands in prehistoric times were referred to as dawn horses. However, at the end of the last Ice Age, nearly 12,000 years ago, they were wiped out. For thousands of years America had no horses, until the Conquistadors arrived from Spain in the 16th Century and brought horses with them. Some of these horses escaped and others were set free, forming the breed known today as the Mustang.

As other settlers came to America, they brought different types of horse and pony, including Morgans and draft breeds such as Percherons, Belgians and Clydesdales. Many of these escaped or were turned loose to join the wild herds, adding their own blood to the already eclectic Mustang.

It's thought that by the end of the 19th Century there were up to two million Mustangs in the United States. Farmers who considered these horses to be pests killed many of them and the number fell to around 25,000.

> STANDARDS

Mustangs are described as sure-footed and having good endurance. They're found in every single colour, including paint and roan. Their mane, tail and lower legs are often black. They usually stand between 14 and 15hh, but there are no breed standard limits. They have extremely strong hooves, making them less prone to leg injuries and hoof ailments than some other breeds.

Mustangs have amazing endurance!

WILD OR NOT WILD?

Mustangs are often referred to as wild, but because they're descended from once-domesticated horses, they should really be called feral, as they're not truly wild.

TEMPERAMENT

Mustangs are known for their intelligence and independent spirit. They usually have a big personality and a mind of their own, but can be very obedient with the correct handling and training. Some might say they're difficult by nature, but Mustangs who are trained by patient and experienced handlers make wonderful riding horses. They can turn their hoof to racing, showing and many other competitive disciplines. These horses demand respect – they have a definite no-nonsense attitude and if you can work with that, then a Mustang could be the horse for you!

WILD HORSES TODAY

In 1971, the United States Congress passed the Wild Free-Roaming Horse and Burro Act, which banned capturing, harming or killing free-roaming horses on public land. The care of the wild horse herds on federal land was turned over to the Bureau of Land Management. Today, about 50,000 wild horses live on private ranches, wildlife refuges, Native American reservations and in sanctuaries.

NAME
The English word mustang comes from the Mexican Spanish word mestengo, which means animal that strays.

DETERMINED DRAY HORSES

Long before lorries were invented, heavy horses pulled drays – large carts used for transporting barrels and other heavy goods. These horses were known as dray horses

Dray horse heyday

Dray horses became common way back in the 18th Century. They were originally used to deliver farm produce, but soon became known for delivering wooden barrels of ale all around the country.

Unfortunately, the use of dray horses declined with the rise of cars and lorries. Machines were cheaper to run and more efficient than horses (cars don't need lunch or a rest!), which meant many industries no longer needed their working horses.

DID YOU KNOW?
Shire horses, on average, measure 17.2hh – that's a lot bigger than Duggie!

HEAVY BREEDS

Shire horses are the most common breed of dray horse, but other heavy horses, such as Clydesdales, are also used. These cold-blooded breeds are best suited for the job due to their sturdy build and docile temperament – you wouldn't want a Thoroughbred galloping off with a delivery!

DID YOU KNOW?
It's estimated that at the start of the 20th Century, there were 150,000 horses used by breweries in the UK – that's a lot of horses!

Clydesdales

Shires

Modern dray horses

A number of breweries have reintroduced the use of dray horses, who carry out local deliveries and visit county shows. Many county shows have different types of heavy horse classes, so you can see dray horses decked out in all their finery. They're a fantastic sight to see!

DID YOU KNOW?
Dray horses in other countries are decorated in different styles – check out these gorgeous horses in Germany!

Famous faces

The Budweiser Clydesdales have become world-famous due to their impressive displays and super-cute television adverts. The company owns more than 250 Clydesdales across America, all measuring at least 18hh!

Bit of bling

Dray horses are often decorated with elaborate plaits, ribbons and brass to make them look super-smart.

Horse brasses are metal discs used to decorate harnesses and there are many unique designs – some dating back hundreds of years. They often commemorate events, such as The Queen's Jubilee, while others show traditional scenes such as farming.

RIDER *psychology*

The way you think when you're around ponies can affect the way they behave. Having a positive mental attitude can actually improve your riding and will benefit your pony, too. Check out how to achieve it with our rider psychology guide

What is psychology?

Psychology is the study of the mind and behaviour. It's about our thoughts and feelings, and how they affect us and make us behave. The way you think has a great impact on your emotions, your body language and how you act – whether you realise it or not!

Rider emotions and behaviour

We experience different emotions every day – it's a normal part of life. However, emotions can easily take over, affect how you think and, when you're around ponies, affect the way you ride and behave towards them, too.

NERVOUS

Everyone feels nervous sometimes. Whether you're worried about a big test at school or a competition you've got coming up, nerves can creep up on you at any time, so it's important to learn how to cope with them.

Nerves can come on suddenly – we've all felt the familiar flutter of butterflies when our instructor asks us to jump a scary fence. The occasional flutter of nerves can actually be a good thing as they help you focus and try harder. However, if you feel nervous all the time when you're riding or handling your pony, that's not such a good thing. Take some time to think about why you're nervous. Getting to the bottom of the reason (as small as it may be!) is important to help you overcome it and conquer your nerves.

Nerves can come on suddenly

Common reasons for feeling nervous include…

● **your pony's behaviour**
If your fave pony is a bit spooky or has a reputation for misbehaving, it can easily make you nervous as you'll be anticipating his naughty behaviour. When you're riding, overcome your nerves by focusing your mind on something else. Why not quietly sing your favourite song to your pony. You'll be preoccupied remembering the words and your soft tone of voice will help keep your pony calm, too.

● **a negative experience**
If you've had a negative experience with your pony, such as a fall, it's understandable that you might be nervous that it could happen again. Instead of thinking about what happened in the past, focus on all the positive experiences you've had with your fave pony rather than the negative ones. Remember that positive experiences build confidence!

● **worrying about what could happen**
We're all guilty of it! It's easy to dream up nightmare scenarios – what if I'm out on a hack and a bird flies out of that bush and my pony takes off? What if my pony stops at a filler and I fall off? But constantly thinking 'what if?' won't benefit you at all, it'll only make you paranoid and your nerves worse. Clearing your mind and focusing on what's actually happening will help you relax and enjoy yourself.

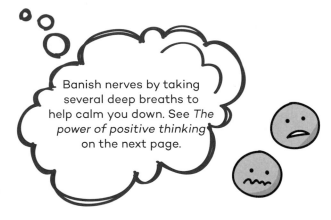

Banish nerves by taking several deep breaths to help calm you down. See *The power of positive thinking* on the next page.

STRESSED

Feeling stressed is really common. It can be caused by feeling under pressure, having lots to do or by feeling nervous for long periods of time.

Your pony can tell when you're stressed or anxious, so unless you've got a super-chilled pony, don't be surprised if he starts acting a little on-edge, too. A stressed rider and a stressed pony isn't a good combination, so if you're feeling really stressed one day, give your pony a groom instead of riding. He'll appreciate it (and be super-clean after!) and you won't risk winding each other up or having an argument.

Remember, riding's a hobby and is supposed to be fun! Spending time with your pony is the perfect way to de-stress, so leave your worries at the yard gate and just concentrate on having a great time with your fave pony.

HAPPY

Everyone loves to feel happy! When you're happy, you're relaxed and worry-free, which your pony will pick up on so he'll feel the same way, too. Plus, when you're happy you can concentrate on having fun with your fave pony – what's better than that?

TOO RELAXED

Being calm and relaxed around your pony is great, but there is such a thing as *too* relaxed. Ponies are clever and if you're not paying attention, many ponies will take advantage. For example, texting your BFF while leading your pony in from the field could see you being dragged off on the end of the leadrope towards a patch of juicy grass! Remember, ponies have a mind of their own and if you're not aware of what he's doing, you could find yourself in a tricky situation, or even put yourself or your pony in danger.

Stay relaxed, as your calm attitude will rub off on your pony, but always have your wits about you and think about what could happen in each situation. Being alert and aware will help keep you both safe at all times.

CONFIDENT

Being confident is great. When you're confident, you'll feel positive and give out good vibes to your pony – so you'll be an unstoppable combo! Being over-confident can be a negative, though, as you could overface yourself and your pony without realising it. Remember that pushing yourself or your pony to progress before you're ready could result in a knock in confidence. If you think you're ready to move up a level, get advice from your riding instructor first to keep your confidence growing.

Relax and smile!

Being too relaxed can be a negative thing

SAD

If you feel down, it'll show in your body language. You might not be aware of it, but the way you walk, act and ride will be different if you're feeling sad or emotional. Ponies can sense when people are upset and it can make them feel worried that there's something to be upset about.

Even if you're having a bad day or going through an emotional time, try to put on a brave face when you visit your pony. Spending time with him is likely to make you feel better and ponies are great listeners! When you're sad, take your pony out for a relaxing hack rather than trying to perfect your moves in the school, as you're less likely to be able to concentrate fully. Plus, a hack in the sunshine is one of the best pick-me-ups there is – fact!

Psychic ponies?

Lots of people wonder why ponies pick up on people's emotions and often adjust their behaviour because of it. Well, ponies are very sensitive and have a great sense of what's going on in their environment. They can read how you're feeling, read your body language and adjust their behaviour accordingly. That's why ponies make great therapy animals for people with disabilities, as they understand humans and have a calming effect.

The power of positive thinking!

Have you ever heard of having a PMA? It stands for positive mental attitude and is something we could all benefit from remembering. It's easy to become disheartened when things aren't going to plan, but if you switch on your PMA, you can turn a negative situation into a positive one. Didn't get the clear round you were hoping for at a show? Instead of being upset, think about how you can improve for next time and be pleased with the fences you jumped well.

Positivity rubs off on your pony, too. Having a 'can-do' attitude will make your pony think he can as well, whereas if you constantly doubt whether you can do something your pony will, too. It's easy to be negative, especially if you're nervous, but try your hardest to remind yourself to think positively – you'll be amazed at what you can achieve!

THE SADDLECLUB SHOWDOWN!

Helena didn't know what she was getting herself and her friends into when she made a bet with the yard next door...

Real life!

A t my yard, Taylor's Lane Farm, there was always a super-friendly atmosphere, and everyone helped out and supported each other, so we never understood what went on at the fancy yard just down the road, TL Equestrian. We'd heard stories of residents sabotaging each others' schooling sessions and not bringing in everyone's ponies when it was pouring with rain.

The proposition

One day, while I was out hacking on my pony, Dennis, I bumped into one of the snooty girls from TL Equestrian, Demi, on her spotless pony, Storm.

"Oh, it's you," Demi smirked as she looked down at us from aboard Storm, who was a good hand taller than Dennis. "You could've given that shabby thing a brush before bringing him out in public," she snarled.

"Whatever, Demi. We'll beat you at the summer show, anyway, just like last year," I bit back. I knew my words would cause a reaction, but I didn't care. Demi was awful to me and my friends at every chance she got, so I liked to remind her of mine and Dennis' proudest moment – winning the open jumping class at the summer show, pushing Demi into second place.

"Ha!" Demi exclaimed. "Storm's a far better pony than Dennis! In fact, our yard saddleclub is better than yours. We'll beat you all at the show, you'll see!"

Before I knew what I was saying, I took her bet. "Fine, our saddleclub versus your saddleclub! It's on!"

Owning up

Back at the yard, I realised I'd dragged my friends into a battle they might not want to be a part of. I felt panicky, until my best friend, Robyn, bounded up to me and grabbed my arm. "Oh my God, Helena! Is it true that you've organised a showdown with that snooty bunch down the road?"

"Erm, yeah..." I said, shakily.

"That's AMAZING! I've been waiting for a chance to show them what we're made of!" Robyn grinned at me and, before I could open my mouth to answer, she continued. "I know Cara will be up for it after that girl, Melody, said last week that Piglet suited his name."

I suddenly felt excited with the support of my friends and my panic quickly faded.

"Okay great, let's do this!" I said, grinning.

We devised a practising schedule, taking it in turns to jump our ponies on alternate days after school, with the two who weren't riding being eyes on the ground.

"Their ponies might be more expensive than ours,

but I know we can do it!" Cara said, as she patted Piglet after our last practice session.

"Three days to go!" Robyn said, "are you ready?"

"Yes!" Cara and I exclaimed together.

Judgement day

The day of the show quickly came around and, as we warmed up, I suddenly felt nervous watching the TL Equestrian girls on their flashy ponies.

I was first to go out of everyone. I rubbed Dennis' neck, pushed him into canter and pointed him at the first fence. He jumped his heart out for an easy clear.

"Yes! A great start!" Cara grinned. "Demi is up next." I turned to watch Demi's round. She and Storm sailed round stylishly, but were a couple of seconds slower.

Another of the TL Equestrian girls, Polly, was next. Another clear. Our two saddleclubs were neck-and-neck as Robyn rode into the ring. They put in a faultless round, too, but were a bit slower than Demi.

TL Equestrian's last rider, Melody, was up. She was going well until her pony spooked at a filler, got too close and knocked the front rail for four faults.

I felt for Cara, as the pressure was really on. A clear round from her and Piglet, and we would win the bet!

Disaster strikes!

Cara started well but then, without warning, Piglet put in a sliding stop at the water tray, sending poor Cara flying straight over his head.

I glanced sheepishly at the TL Equestrian girls, expecting them to be laughing their heads off, but instead, they were busy arguing over the reason for Melody's four faults and hadn't seen Cara's fall.

Back at the lorry, Robyn and I comforted Cara.

"I can't believe I let you down," Cara wiped her eyes. "Don't worry! Who cares about the bet, anyway?" Robyn said. I realised I'd made a mistake by putting pressure on my friends and our ponies. "It's supposed to be fun, right? We can't help it if those girls don't think that way. I mean, look at them!"

We looked over to the TL Equestrian lorry, where the girls were still arguing.

"At least we're not like them!" Robyn said.

"Thanks, guys," Cara sniffed. "So we're the real winners, then?"

I nodded, but Robyn shrugged. "Or maybe we're all losers?" she said, with a cheeky grin. We all giggled and my stupid bet was forgotten.

CAN'T HACK, WON'T HACK!

Eloise and her friends love riding together and have loads of fun in the school. But when it comes to hacking out, Eloise is always left behind...

Hi Eloise! Are you schooling Bumble today?

Hey, Charley. Yeah, we're working on our transitions.

Great session, guys!

Buzz's square halts are really coming on. Shall we ride together again tomorrow?

Fab! I'll tell Sophia and we'll join you.

We should totally go on a hack!

YEAH!

But you just agreed to ride with us!

Yeah, and you said you were busy last time we went for a hack. You only ever ride Bumble in the school, give him a break!

Carina and Albi
as **Charley and Lilly**

Katie and Nemo
as **Sophia and Buzz**

Millie and Sean
as **Eloise and Bumble**

QUIZ

To eat OR NOT TO EAT?

It's important to protect your fave pony from poisonous plants. Test your knowledge of them with our mini quiz and brush up on your facts!

FACT!
Yew is so poisonous to ponies that, even in small quantities, it causes sudden death, and is still toxic when it's dried.

Essential knowledge!
It's important to be aware of the signs of poisoning. They include...

- loss of co-ordination
- diarrhoea
- producing more saliva than normal
- inability to pass droppings
- muscle contractions causing sudden movement
- colic
- sensitive skin in sunlight

Which plants are poisonous?
The following plants are some of the most poisonous to ponies and are commonly found in areas where ponies might graze. They are...

- ragwort
- oak (acorns)
- yew
- St John's wort
- sycamore (seeds)
- bracken
- box
- nightshade
- rhododendron

FACT!
The seeds of sycamore trees, which are poisonous to ponies, are responsible for causing an often fatal condition called atypical myopathy. It's important to clear up sycamore seeds that fall in your pony's field, – as they can spread a long way – and section off the area they fall in so he can't eat them.

TOP TIP!
Always try to remove poisonous plants from your pony's paddock, but if it's not possible – for example, if it would involve removing a large tree – keep ponies away from poisonous trees, plants or hedgerows by using electric fencing to section off the area. Leave at least two metres between the poisonous plant and the fence.

☠ ST JOHN'S WORT

☠ BOX

☠ RHODODENDRON

1 Which of these can be addictive to ponies?

(A) acorns ✓

B leaves

C Chocolate

2. Why might ponies be tempted to eat poisonous plants?

A they like to eat plants that are colourful and interesting

B if you don't feed them at the same time each day ✓

(C) their grazing is poor and they're really hungry

3. Which common poisonous plant should be pulled up and burnt to stop its seeds spreading?

A birch ✓

(B) ragwort

C foxglove

4. Which food that most humans like to eat and grows in the ground can be dangerous to ponies if they eat new shoots?

A sweetcorn ✓

(B) potatoes

C cocoa beans

5. St John's wort is poisonous to ponies, but when it's processed, what is it commonly used for?

A decoration

B dog food ✓

(C) human medicine

6. Plants on parade! Can you identify these five poisonous plants?
Award yourself one point if you get one or two correct answers, two points for three or four correct and three points for all five!

bracken ✓   ragwort ✓   nightshade

yew ✓

Points = 3   oak acorns ✓

TURN TO PAGE 100 FOR THE ANSWERS!

MY SCORE

0-3 CORRECT
Uh-oh, your knowledge of poisonous plants needs improving. But don't worry – use our fab facts and issues of PONY to boost your knowledge. You'll be a pro in no time!

4-5 CORRECT
Well done, you know a fair bit about poisonous plants, but you're not an expert yet. Swot up on all the info you can get your hands on, then take our test again. You're bound to get full marks!

6-8 CORRECT
Wow, you're a poisonous plants genius! No sneaky bit of ragwort or nightshade will grow in your fave pony's field under your keen eye. Keep up the good work!

SPOTLIGHT ON...

Hello Sanctos

Meet Britain's best showjumper!

Stable name: Sanctos • Discipline: Showjumping
Ridden by: Scott Brash

Born in Belgium, Hello Sanctos was originally called Sanctos van het Gravenhof. Now the bay gelding has the famous 'Hello' prefix that almost all horses owned by Lord and Lady Harris and Lord and Lady Kirkham have – in fact, six of his stablemates are 'Hello' horses!

Sanctos has racked up loads of frequent flyer miles in his career as a top showjumper. He's competed in America, the Middle East and all over Europe, and spends most of the year travelling to new and exciting locations. Luckily, he loves to travel on planes!

Dream horse

Rider Scott Brash dreamed of being a top showjumper since he was seven years old and it was Sanctos who made his dream a reality. He was bought in 2011 for Scott to contest the Olympics with and the pair quickly bonded. The London 2012 Olympics cemented their place in the history books, as the team won Britain its first showjumping gold medal since 1952!

Home comforts

When he's not winning competitions all over the world, Sanctos loves to come home and chill out. He's known for sleeping all day and often has to be persuaded to get up for a ride.

Sanctos takes his 'me time' very seriously and likes to be left alone in his stable to snooze. He prefers to be given fuss when he's just done a fab job in the ring – in which case he loves a Polo or a banana from his owners!

Scott likes to turn Sanctos out in the field whenever he can, as he's so chilled out and happy in there that Scott never has to worry about him misbehaving.

Plaiting panic

Scott's groom Hannah plaits Sanctos for shows – but only for the most important classes, as he seems to understand that being plaited means he has a big day ahead of him. He gets a bit nervous and starts to shake his head, so Hannah prefers to plait him only when she has to and lets him chill out the rest of the time.

Any other time he's the most relaxed horse on the yard and isn't bothered by the electric atmosphere at shows. In fact, he's so calm that he has to be persuaded to go anywhere – unless he spots some grass, in which case he drags Hannah over for a graze!

THE LAST STRAW
Hello Sanctos likes to have a really thick straw bed to lie down on. Sometimes he can be caught nibbling on it while having a nap!

RECORD BREAKERS

☆ Sanctos and Scott are the first duo to win the Rolex Grand Slam of Showjumping. To scoop the €1.3million total prize, they won at Geneva, Aachen and Calgary in 2015.

 The fab pair have also won a record-breaking three Global Champions Tour Grands Prix – in London, Paris and Portugal in 2014.

BEST FRIENDS

Sanctos loves to hang out with his stablemates Hello M'Lady and Ursula XII – both Grand Prix showjumpers. Perhaps they discuss tactics!

TOP RESULTS

2015 Rolex Grand Slam - winner
2014 Global Champions Tour Series - champion
2013 Global Champions Tour Series - champion
2013 Herning European Championships - team gold, individual bronze
2012 London Olympics - team gold, 5th individually

★

DID YOU KNOW?

Hello Sanctos used to be owned by another Olympian – American rider Peter Wylde.

LIKES

- going out in the field
- Polos – he'll do anything for a mint and his owners, Lady Harris and Lady Kirkham, always have a packet on hand
- bananas
- travelling by plane – he's been all over the world
- his me time – he likes to be left alone in his bed to chill out

DISLIKES

- being clipped – he'd never dream of kicking, but he has very sensitive skin, so it makes him really tense

HAVE FUN
cross-country

Going cross-country is about the most fun you can have with your fave pony! Find out how to ace it every time

TOP TIP!

Shorten your stirrups a couple of holes before you go cross-country. You'll be in galloping position between jumps, so short stirrups will help you stay out of the saddle.

TOP TACK

Your pony needs to be properly kitted out for cross-country. Ride him in a normal GP or jumping saddle, but it's a good idea to add...

● **protective boots** – front and back boots protect your pony's legs from scrapes, and overreach boots will help prevent him pulling off a shoe and overreach injuries

● **neckstrap or breastplate** – add a running martingale attachment if you think your pony will get strong. Having a neckstrap or breastplate gives you something to grab onto if you need to!

● **a stronger bit** – lots of ponies can go cross-country in their usual bit, but if your pony gets strong, ask your instructor to help you choose a different bit

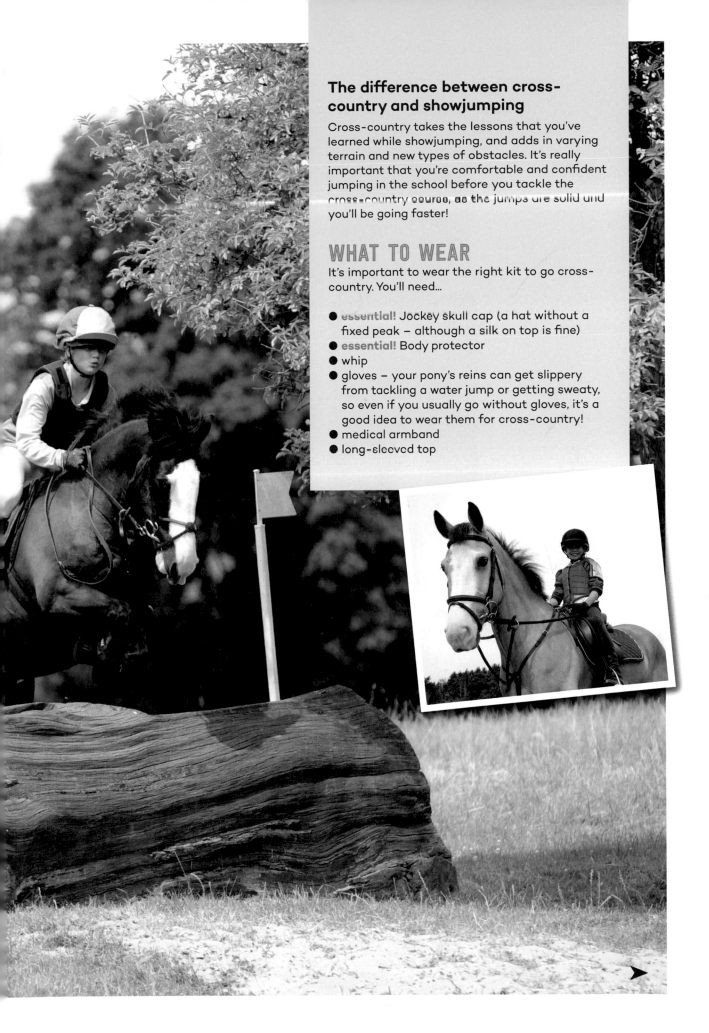

The difference between cross-country and showjumping

Cross-country takes the lessons that you've learned while showjumping, and adds in varying terrain and new types of obstacles. It's really important that you're comfortable and confident jumping in the school before you tackle the cross-country course, as the jumps are solid and you'll be going faster!

WHAT TO WEAR

It's important to wear the right kit to go cross-country. You'll need...

- **essential!** Jockey skull cap (a hat without a fixed peak – although a silk on top is fine)
- **essential!** Body protector
- whip
- gloves – your pony's reins can get slippery from tackling a water jump or getting sweaty, so even if you usually go without gloves, it's a good idea to wear them for cross-country!
- medical armband
- long-sleeved top

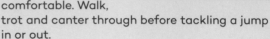

TYPES OF FENCE AND HOW TO RIDE THEM

Part of what makes cross-country jumping so fun is all the different types of fence you'll encounter!

Logs Cross-country courses feature logs of all shapes and sizes. They make a great warm-up fence and should be ridden like an oxer, with a forward canter.

Steps and drops It's important to ride straight so your pony can work out what he's meant to do. Approach at a walk or trot the first few times and keep your pony moving forward. When jumping up a step, get into a secure jumping position and move your hands up your pony's neck to allow him to stretch out. To tackle a drop, let your reins slide through your fingers as your pony pops down and think about bringing your upper body back. Your position for a drop is perfect when your pony could disappear from underneath you and you'd still land on your feet!

Corners The best way to tackle a corner is to imagine that a pole has been placed straight across it, from the narrowest end to the widest. Keep this imaginary pole in mind as you approach it and jump it like a vertical. Make sure you ride straight to the jump, staying closer to the narrower end, otherwise it might be too wide for your pony and he'll struggle to clear it. Don't get too close to the narrow end, though, or he could run out!

Water Since ponies can't tell how deep water is, they rely on you for confidence when tackling obstacles in the water. Allow your pony to walk around in the water until he's comfortable. Walk, trot and canter through before tackling a jump in or out.

Ditches Tackle ditches in a positive trot, in case your pony wants to have a look. Sit up tall, kick on and look ahead – you don't need to get into a proper jumping position when popping a ditch, but remember to give with your hands and allow with your upper body so you don't bump your pony in the mouth or on his back.

Skinny fences Skinnies require a good line, so make sure you look where you're going and ride positively!

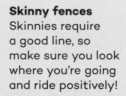

Changing your position

Because your pony has to canter much further and quite a bit faster around a cross-country course, it's important to tweak your position to make it easier for him and less tiring for you. Push your weight into your heels and allow your knees to press into the knee rolls, then lift your bottom a little bit out of the saddle. You shouldn't be sitting in the saddle, but don't stand in your stirrups, either.

Shorten your reins a little and push your hands forward to keep a steady, even contact.

Get the right canter

When you're going cross-country, your pony needs a more active canter than you'd use when jumping in the school. Think of going a little bit faster and encourage him to take bigger strides. This will help him to meet the jumps comfortably and jump them easily. Practise adjusting your pony's canter from a big, fast canter to a shorter, bouncy one, so you can easily adjust it when you need to.

Warming up

Cross-country is hard work for your pony, so make sure you warm him up really well before you tackle any courses. Trotting in the field is a really good workout for him and you can use your warm-up time to practise changing your canter stride before you get out on the course.

When you're ready to start jumping, pick an easy log or a small upright as a warm-up fence and pop it on both reins. Use your warm-up jump as a good excuse to practise your straightness and accuracy. Then you'll find jumping skinnies and corners easy!

Practice makes perfect

If you've not been cross-country before, practise with a friend on an experienced pony. This will help you see what to do and also give you and your pony confidence.

TOP TIP!
Always look for the next fence, even if it's a long way away – this will help you ride the best line from one fence to the next.

Wet feet!

If your pony isn't keen to go into water, don't panic. It's normal for ponies to be cautious when they can't see the bottom and he must learn to trust you. Build his trust by reassuring him, not telling him off.

It's a good idea to ask your friend to give you a lead through the water to show your pony it's safe.

Problem solving

Cross-country can be really exciting, partly because it doesn't always go to plan! Here are some of the problems you may encounter and how to solve them.

Strong pony If your pony is tanking off with you, ask him for lots of trot and canter transitions to get him to listen. Trot him into the jumps, then gently bring him back to trot after he lands – that way he'll start paying attention to what's happening on his back!

Nervous pony If your pony is worried about any of the new jumps that he's encountering, ask a friend with an experienced pony for a lead. He'll be more concerned with following his friend than worrying about the jump!

Nervous rider Cross-country isn't about jumping the biggest fences on the course, so don't feel under pressure to jump anything that you feel is too big. You can learn loads and have fun flying over smaller fences, too! Start small and work your way up as it becomes easier.

Cooling down

After a successful cross-country session, you and your pony will probably be pretty tired! It's important to cool your pony down as carefully as you warmed him up, so don't come straight down to walk from canter – let him catch his breath in trot for a minute or two, then bring him back to walk on a long rein. Don't forget to give him a big pat for a job well done!

TOP TIP!
Cross-country isn't all about zooming around at top speed – it's important to think about control, balance and straightness, just like when you're showjumping. You can allow your pony to pick up the pace between jumps, but when you're aiming for a fence, bring him back to a forward-going, bouncy canter.

HOOF

how-to

HANDLING

Be a pro at picking up, cleaning out and looking after your pony's hooves with our fab guide!

Hoofcare basics

Hooves should be checked at least once a day, as changes can happen quickly. Check the hoof wall, frog and sole for any changes. Look at the condition of his shoes and pick out any mud or stones using a hoofpick.

TOP TIP!

When you pick out your pony's feet, check that nothing is stuck down the side of his frog.

HANDLING HOW-TO

It's important to know how to pick up your pony's feet correctly, not only so you can pick them out and check them properly, but also for safety – ponies' feet are heavy and can move very fast! Follow our step-by-step guide...

Step 1
Make sure your pony is tied up securely with a quick-release knot.

Step 2
Start with a front leg. Approach your pony and place your hand on his shoulder so he knows what you're intending to do. Talk quietly to reassure him.

Step 3
Stand parallel to your pony's foreleg and run your hand down the back of his leg so he doesn't get a shock when you ask him to lift his foot up. When picking up his hindlegs, run your hand down the front of his leg instead.

Step 4
When your hand gets below his knee, move it to the front of his leg so your arm isn't in the way of your pony lifting his foot.

WATCHPOINT!
Don't stand facing your pony's head and try to lift his foot, because he could catch you with his leg if he lifts it suddenly.

Step 5
Once your pony has lifted up his foot, take hold of it with the hand that's nearest to him by placing your hand underneath his hoof so you've got a secure hold.

Step 6
When you've checked or picked out your pony's hoof, place it gently back on the ground – don't just let it go! He'll be much more willing to pick up his feet if you handle them carefully.

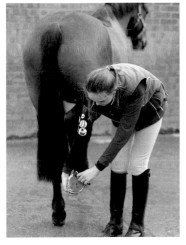

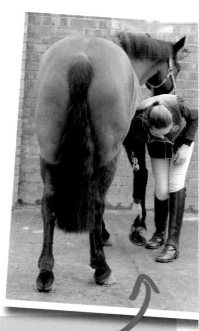

Step 7
Repeat steps two to six with the other three feet.

Picking out feet
It's important to pick out your pony's feet when he comes in from the field, and before and after you ride him, to remove stones and impacted mud from his hooves.

Use your hoofpick in a downwards motion, never upwards, or you could risk catching his sensitive frog.

Checking shoes
Ponies should have a visit from the farrier every five to eight weeks. However, sometimes shoes can become loose between farrier visits. Check each of your pony's shoes when you pick out his feet. Make sure the clenches (the end of the nails) aren't protruding, the shoes aren't thinner in some places than others and that the side wall and heel haven't grown too long so they stick out over the shoe.

On the lookout
There's a range of problems that could affect your pony's hooves, but not all of them are obvious. Some signs to look out for are...

Feel for heat

- **heat in the hoof wall, frog or sole of the foot**
- **strong smells**
- **changes in colour**
- **cracks in the hoof wall**

If you're unsure about the condition of your pony's shoes or feet, ask your instructor to double check them or call your farrier for advice.

TOP TIP!
If your pony is reluctant to lift up his foot, gently lean into him to encourage him to shift his weight onto the other side and lift his foot. Some ponies might try to lean their weight onto you to counteract your weight. If your pony does this, you might need to ask an adult to help you.

DID YOU KNOW?
There's an old saying popular among farriers that goes 'no foot, no horse'. It means that if your pony's feet aren't healthy, you won't be able to get the best out of him.

TOP TIP!
Remember to book your farrier in every five to eight weeks to trim your pony's feet. Keep a calendar at the yard and mark it up a couple of weeks before your pony is due for a visit, so you can book an appointment in plenty of time.

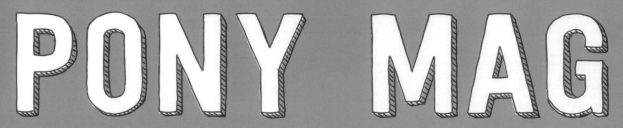

PONY MAG

MORE RIDING, MORE PONY CARE, MORE FUN!

Be a better rider with our fantastic riding features and online videos

Learn everything you need to know about pony care

Keep up to date with the latest rider gossip and behind-the-scenes horsey action

hand made

Make! FUNKY PHONE SOCKS

Jazz up your phone with a cool phone sock, PONY style!

You will need...
- ☑ one sock
- ☑ scissors
- ☑ needle
- ☑ thread
- ☑ fabric glue
- ☑ felt
- ☑ googly eyes
- ☑ fabric paint
- ☑ any other decorations you like!

How to do it!

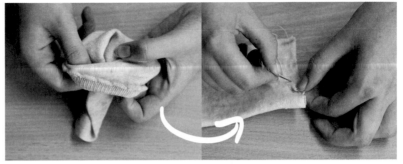

Step 1
Using your phone as a measure, cut the foot off your sock. Leave 0.5cm of space at both ends and make sure your line is straight.

Step 2
Turn the sock inside out and sew along the edge you've just cut. Then turn it back the right way. **Ask an adult for help with sewing if you're unsure**.

Step 3
To decorate your phone sock, draw the outline of your design onto paper and cut it out. Use this as a stencil to cut your design out from felt – why not use the same colour as your fave pony?

Step 4
Glue the felt onto your sock and allow it to dry. Then glue on any additional decorations, such as the eyes and forelock.

Step 5
Sew the beads on to spell your fave pony's name or use fabric paint to write it on.

STEP 5

GET CREATIVE... You don't have to use felt and beads. Check out these cool designs that use glitter, fabric paint, sequins and gems!

BREEDS
>> MARWARI

A rare horse breed from India with amazing ears

Pinto is a popular colour

> HISTORY

The Rathores, traditional rulers of the Marwar region of western India, were the first to breed the Marwari in the 12th Century. The breed was developed by crossing Indian pony breeds with Arabian horses. No one really knows how the Arabian horses came to India, but one legend says that an Arabian ship, containing seven Arabian horses of good breeding, was shipwrecked off the Indian coast. These horses were used as foundation bloodstock for the Marwari.

The Rathores followed a very strict breeding policy that promoted purity and hardiness in the breed. As a result, the horses were renowned for their bravery and courage in battle, as well as their loyalty to their riders.

However, the breed fell out of fashion and was near extinction by 1950. It was saved by a handful of enthusiasts who continued breeding and founded a group called Marwari Bloodlines. They worked with the Indian government to promote the breed and even took some Marwari horses to the United States to raise awareness.

> STANDARDS

They usually stand at 15-16hh, but can be as small as 14hh and as tall as 17hh. Marwari horses can be any colour, although pinto is particularly popular with breeders. The best horses are slender but well-built, long-limbed and muscular. Their coats are fine and silky. Even though they have long legs, they have quite small hooves. The most amazing and unusual thing about Marwaris is their ears, which turn inwards and often touch at the tips.

Marwaris are quite a hardy breed and easy to keep, but they can have a flighty and unpredictable temperament. Most owners consider them a one-person horse.

USES

Marwaris are often crossed with Thoroughbreds to produce a larger, more versatile horse. They've been known to do well at dressage and are often used to play polo, sometimes playing against Thoroughbreds. They're also often used for endurance riding and horseback safaris.

Within the Marwari breed was a strain known as the Natchni, believed by local people to be born to dance. Decorated in silver, jewels and bells, these horses were trained to perform complex prancing and leaping movements at many ceremonies, including weddings. Although the Natchni strain is extinct today, horses trained in these skills are still in demand in rural India.

QUIZ

GET A HANDLE ON IT

Are you a horse whisperer in the making or are you in need of some practice? Find out with our fab handling quiz! Follow Jessie as she spends a day at the yard with her fave pony, Casper, and help her with her handling skills

1. It's Saturday morning and that means only one thing – a whole day for Jessie to spend with her fave ponies at the yard! First, though, she has to get dressed. **List five things she should wear to keep herself safe when handling ponies.**

helmet, gloves, boots & smallhee jodse, long sleeved top

2. Jessie arrives at the yard and has a look at the lesson rota. She's down to ride Casper, her fave pony – result! First, though, she's got to get him in from the field. **What should she do?**

A Catch one of his companions instead – Casper will follow and she can let him slip out of the gate with his friend!

B Approach him as quickly as possible, so he doesn't have time to run away. ✓

C Approach him slowly and from the side, with the leadrope behind her back. If he's really hard to catch, she should try holding a treat in her hand and offering it to him when she gets close – but not forgetting to be careful of his greedy friends!

3. Phew! Jessie has caught Casper, and now she can get back to the yard and get ready for her jumping lesson. But hang on a sec – it looks like she's been daydreaming about winning the Hickstead Derby and she's stopped paying attention to what she's doing! **How many mistakes can you spot?**

5

4. Jessie's instructor, Lisa, calls her over to help with something, so she puts Casper in his stable. **How should she lead him through the doorway?** ✓

A Walk into the stable ahead of him, keeping an eye on him to make sure he doesn't tread on her.

B Walk through the doorway alongside him, making sure he doesn't hit his hip on the frame.

C Ask him to back up into the stable so that he can't turn his hindquarters towards her.

5. Jessie finds her instructor talking to the farrier. "There you are!" Lisa says. "I'm afraid I'm a bit busy at the moment – could you please hold Buttercup while the farrier trims her feet?" **What does Jessie need to remember while holding Buttercup?** ✓

A To stand on the same side as the farrier so that if Buttercup misbehaves, her hindquarters will swing away from the farrier.

B To keep a handful of pony nuts in her pocket in case Buttercup gets bored and take some pics for her Instagram – she's really cute!

C To let Buttercup lean her head on the farrier – she won't be able to balance otherwise.

6. The farrier's all done and Buttercup's feet are looking fab! Now it's time to focus on Casper – Jessie's got a lesson to get ready for! **Underline all the things that are wrong in this story.**

Jessie stops by the tack room on her way to Casper's stable and grabs his saddle, bridle and a numnah. She heads back to his stable and puts his saddle over the stable door. There's a grooming kit outside Casper's stable, so she grabs a few brushes and drops them over the door. Then she goes into the stable and puts Casper's bridle on him so that she can keep hold of him. He's still munching away at his hay, anyway, so he's not likely to move!

Jessie's first job is to pick out Casper's feet, because he spent the night in the field and has picked up dirt and stones. First, she picks out his nearside hooves, and then she reaches underneath his belly to pick out his offside front hoof. When she reaches behind him to try to grab his offside hind hoof, he shifts his weight over and picks up the nearside hoof – which

she's already picked out – so she gives him a smack on the bottom to tell him off.

Casper's coat is dirty after his night in the field, so Jessie gets to work on him. She wants him to be gleaming for her lesson! Luckily, she grabbed a metal curry comb from the grooming kit – dried mud won't stand a chance! Casper must be a bit ticklish, because he moves away from her. Jessie grabs Casper's reins and gives them a tug to remind him of his manners.

When all the mud is off, Jessie turns around to grab his saddle off the door, and swings it onto his back. She walks behind him to get to his other side and fastens the girth. With Casper tacked up and ready to go, Jessie leaves the reins over his neck and leads him from the offside out of the stable, kicking the brushes out of the way as she goes.

7. Jessie and Casper worked really hard during their lesson, and even jumped a scary filler – result! **What's the first thing Jessie should do after untacking?**

A Grab a cold drink and a snack – luckily, she put a can of lemonade and a chocolate bar in the yard fridge when she arrived!

B Tie Casper up, fill a bucket with cool (but not freezing cold!) water and sponge off his sweaty areas, before popping a cooler on him while he dries.

C Put his stable rug on him so that he can dry off without catching a chill.

8. Jessie would like to give Casper a treat to thank him for being such a good boy. **What's the best way to give it to him?**

A Put it in his feed bowl, tuck it into his haynet, or offer it to him from the palm of her hand, keeping her hand flat, fingers together and thumb in.

B Put a carrot between her teeth and try to get him to take it from her – it's a really funny trick!

C Put it in his bed – it'll give him something to do.

9. Lisa finds Jessie in Casper's stable and asks if she wouldn't mind helping out with the next lesson. She needs her to lead Topsy, who's being ridden by a beginner. **How should Jessie lead Topsy?**

A Hold onto the reins as close to the bit as possible. This will give her extra control.

B Pass a leadrope through the bit ring nearest her and clip it to the opposite side, or clip it onto his noseband. This gives her control without interfering with the rider's aids.

C Use a lunge rein and wrap it tightly around her hands so that if Topsy shies, she won't lose control and scare the rider.

10. What a day! It's nearly time to head home, but first Jessie has to sort out Casper. **What should she do to make sure he's happy and comfortable?**

A Take his feed into the stable, waving her arms at him to stop him from barging. While he's eating, skip out his bed into a wheelbarrow.

B Take him out of the stable and tie him up on the yard. Make sure the rope is long enough that he can reach his feed bucket on the floor. When he's finished, turn him out and go home – she can muck out tomorrow.

C Take him out of his stable and tie him up on the yard. Skip out his bed and top up his water. Put his feed in his manger and then bring him back into his stable, turning him to face the doorway before she removes his headcollar.

TO FIND OUT HOW YOU GOT ON, CHECK OUT PAGES 100-101.

On her way home, Jessie thinks back on yet another blissful, pony-filled day. She reckons she might be a bit of a pony pro by now!

SUMMER CAMP SHOCK

Evie finally got the chance to go to camp with her friends, but would it be everything she expected?

The alarm rang and I leapt out of bed. As I was pulling on my jodhpurs, butterflies fluttered in my tummy. The day had finally arrived. Every summer, my riding school held a camp. There were lessons, hacks and competitions, and everyone slept over in tents in one of the fields. I couldn't wait to be part of the action. I'd booked my favourite pony, Felix, and for months I'd been dreaming of treating him like my very own. I couldn't wait.

I flung the car door open when Mum pulled up at the stables and ran towards the group of girls huddled on the yard, all giggling excitedly about the upcoming camp. I spotted Felix's head over his stable door, so decided to take a quick detour and give him a good morning kiss on the nose. As I peered into his stable and stroked his neck, I noticed his back legs were all bandaged up, then I heard the familiar voice of my instructor, Sarah. "I'm afraid I have some bad news," she said. "Felix was kicked in the field yesterday and he's lame, so you won't be able to ride him for the camp. But don't worry, you can still take part with Dexter, he hasn't got a rider."

Disappointment

My heart sank, and not just because my dream of having Felix for the camp wouldn't be coming true. There was a reason Dexter didn't have a rider. The little bay was possibly the naughtiest pony on the planet. Not only did he pull horrible faces, bite and kick, but

he wasn't much fun to ride, either. He had a habit of stopping in the middle of the school and refusing to move. But, as disappointed as I was, there wasn't much I could do about it.

Dodging the gnashing teeth, I glumly got Dexter ready for the first part of the day – a jumping lesson. While warming up, I felt increasingly grumpy and my legs began to ache after only two laps of the school – Dexter was such hard work. Jumping wasn't his favourite and after getting over only five jumps, he threw in the towel and performed his signature trick – parking himself in the middle of the school. Dexter had decided that my jumping session was over. I couldn't help but feel like this camp wasn't going to be much fun at all.

Not all fun and games

The next couple of days were much the same, with Dexter deciding exactly what we would and wouldn't be doing. Even when I was doing my best to make him look smart, he made it very clear that he didn't want my company or attention – he wouldn't even take a carrot from me. The other girls were finding it all very amusing, which made me feel even worse.

Every evening, we all played games and that cheered me up a bit. On the third night, after a great game of rounders, we sat in the tent just before bedtime with torches under our chins, taking it in turns to tell ghost stories. Three stories in and we were all starting to feel a bit freaked out, although no one was going to admit it. Next it was my turn and I told a tale I'd heard at a friend's sleepover. I had everyone's attention.

Up to old tricks

Dexter decided when riding was over

Suddenly, we heard a twig snap outside the tent. Hearts pounding, we sat in silence, listening carefully. Then we heard footsteps making their way round to the front of the tent. The tent door moved and we all gasped, torches shining towards it. A little bay nose poked under the tent doorway. "Dexter!" We all exclaimed, then fell about laughing with relief. I must have forgotten to close his stable door properly.

I went down to the yard in the dark to collect his headcollar so I could put him back to bed. As I walked back into the field towards Dexter, I heard the other girls in the tent talking. "I'm soooo glad I haven't got Dexter, he's such a horrible pony," Amy said.

Catherine replied, "Me too, it was so funny when he just stopped in the school earlier!"

"She'll never get one of the rosettes," Jasmine joined in. I had no idea they'd been talking about me behind my back. Rosettes were given out at the end of the camp for various different things, including best rider, most improved, cleanest pony and the coveted Best in Camp rosette, which everyone had their eye on. They were right, though, I didn't stand a chance of winning anything.

A great escape

Feeling sad, I slipped on Dexter's headcollar while he put his ears back and wrinkled his nose at me. On the way back to his stable, a tear escaped down my cheek. Camp wasn't at all like I'd hoped it would be. Even with Dexter safely back in his stable, I couldn't face going back to join the others, so I sat on one of the banks in his stable and rested my head on my knees. The tears started to come and, once they started, there was no stopping them. Then I felt a warm tickling on the back of my head. It was Dexter, not pulling horrible faces at me, but with his ears forward, gently blowing warm air on me. I reached up and stroked his nose and he stood there, seeming to enjoy it. I'd had a breakthrough. He'd not behaved like this with anyone else before. It'd been quite a rocky road, but maybe we'd finally become friends.

Suddenly, there was a noise and some voices coming from the tack room. Who would be in there at this time of night? There were bales of shavings outside the stables ready for the morning so I slipped out of Dexter's stable and hid behind a bale near his door to get a better look. Two men emerged from the tack room, arms loaded with saddles. We were being burgled! With that, Dexter burst out of his stable

onto the yard. Oh no, not again! I thought, telling myself off for not shutting the door for a second time. Then, to my amazement, Dexter cantered straight for the men, pulling his nastiest face and baring his teeth. Shocked, the men dropped the saddles and ran up the track to a van parked outside the gate.

I ran over to Dexter and flung my arms around him, kissing his neck – he was a hero! I delved into my pocket and found a piece of carrot that had been there since the start of camp. Dexter ate it like it was the most delicious thing ever. Hearing voices behind me, I turned around to see the other girls and my instructor, Sarah, who'd come down to see what all the commotion was. I told the story and at first no one believed me, but when I pointed to the pile of saddles on the yard, their eyes widened in amazement.

History made!

We didn't get any sleep that night, as we kept reliving the evening's events. I didn't tell the girls I'd heard them talking about me, though. It didn't matter anymore – my special moment with Dexter had made up for all the disappointments.

The next morning, it was the end of camp and, after the police had been to take details of the attempted burglary the night before, it was time for Sarah to give out the rosettes. Knowing I wouldn't be getting any, I sat back and cheered the others on as they collected theirs. Everyone had done well and was looking pleased with their collection of ribbons. The last one to be given out was the Best in Camp rosette. Everyone was waiting eagerly to hear if it would be them.

I didn't hear my name when Sarah first called it out, but I realised that everyone was looking at me. "You and Dexter are best in camp!" Sarah said. Amazed, I stood up and collected the big, golden rosette. "But why?" I asked. "We didn't do much riding and Dexter hardly let me groom him."

"Maybe not," said Sarah "but you've been brave and stuck it out with a tough pony, plus you saved all our tack!" The girls all came over cheering and patting me on the back. The rosette was the icing on the cake, but deep down it could never match how special it felt to bond with Dexter. Felix would always be my favourite but, unexpectedly, Dexter was now a very close second. One thing was for sure, this summer camp was going down in history!

Dexter and I are bffs now!

THE ANSWERS

Are you desperate to know how you did in the quizzes? Wait no longer - you'll find all the answers on this page!

PAGES 50-51

WHAT'S YOUR PONY'S PERSONALITY?

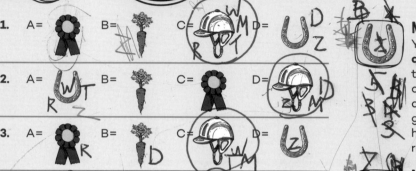

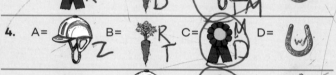

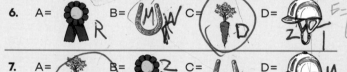

MOSTLY HORSESHOES
Your fave pony is a **drama queen**! He loves nothing more than being the centre of attention and can be a bit of a show-off! However, he hates getting muddy, dirty or wet and has been known to slightly over react to some situations.

MOSTLY RIDING HATS
This pony is one **cool customer**! He's the pony everybody wants because he's good at everything! Nothing fazes him and your instructor calls him Mr Reliable – he's the perfect pony to boost your confidence!

MOSTLY ROSETTES
Call him Speedy Gonzales – your pony is a **speed merchant**! There's nothing he loves more than going fast. He's great at jumping, although you might get time penalties for going too fast cross-country! He's not keen on schooling or dressage and would rather go for a fast hack with lots of gallops instead.

MOSTLY CARROTS
Your fave pony is a **nosy parker**. He's got to know what's going on at all times! He sometimes struggles to concentrate on what you're asking him and can be a bit spooky. But he never misses a trick!

PAGES 80-81

TO EAT OR NOT TO EAT?

1. A **2.** C **3.** B **4.** B **5.** C

6. 1 bracken, 2 ragwort, 3 yew, 4 nightshade, 5 oak (acorn)

PAGES 96-97

GET A HANDLE ON IT!

1. Gloves, boots with a small heel, jodhpurs, an up-to-standard riding hat and a long-sleeved top. Jessie can also wear a body protector and a jacket, and should tie her long hair up so that it doesn't get caught on anything.

2. C

3. There are five main handling mistakes here...

- Jessie's on the phone
- She's not paying attention to Casper
- She's holding the rope with one hand
- She's letting Casper graze
- She isn't wearing a hat

4. B

5. A

6. **Did you spot the mistakes Jessie made tacking up Casper? Here's what she should have done...**

Jessie stops by the tack room on her way to Casper's stable and picks up his saddle, bridle and a numnah. She heads back to his stable and places his tack on a saddle rack so that it won't fall and get damaged. She picks out the brushes she needs from her grooming kit and places them outside the stable. Then she goes into the stable and quietly approaches Casper's head before putting his headcollar on and tying him to a loop of baling twine attached to the wall.

Jessie's first job is to pick out Casper's feet. First, she picks out his nearside hooves, then she moves round to Casper's offside by moving slowly around the front of him, letting him know where she is by talking to him. Then she picks out his offside hooves.

Casper's coat is dirty after his night in the field, so Jessie gets to work grooming him. She uses a metal curry comb to clean her brushes as they get dirty. Casper shifts his weight towards Jessie, so she asks him to move over by pressing her fingers against his side.

When all the mud is off, Jessie leaves the stable and puts her brushes back in the grooming kit, before collecting Casper's saddle from the rack. She attaches the numnah to his saddle before placing the saddle slightly above his wither and sliding it back into place. She fastens the girth on the near side before passing quietly in front of him to fasten the girth on the offside. Then she unclips his leadrope, undoes his headcollar and refastens it around his neck, then places his reins over his head to stop him from moving away as she puts his bridle on. Once his bridle is on, she removes his headcollar and hangs it up. With Casper tacked up and ready to go, Jessie leads him out of the stable with his reins over his head, taking care to lead him straight so he doesn't bang his hip on the doorframe as she walks him through.

7. B **9.** B

8. A **10.** C

THE MISADVENTURES OF CHARLIE!